Cambridge Tracts in Mathematics
and Mathematical Physics

General Editors

G. H. HARDY, M.A., F.R.S.
E. CUNNINGHAM, M.A.

No. 23

OPERATIONAL METHODS IN MATHEMATICAL PHYSICS

OPERATIONAL METHODS
IN MATHEMATICAL PHYSICS

BY

HAROLD JEFFREYS, M.A., D.Sc., F.R.S.

SECOND EDITION

STECHERT-HAFNER SERVICE AGENCY
New York and London
1964

Originally published in 1927
Second edition 1931
by Cambridge University Press

Reprinted by Arrangement

An amplified form of this tract was published in 1947.
The 3rd edition (1956) of this work is available under
the title of "*Methods of Mathematical Physics.*"

Printed and Published by
Stechert-Hafner Service Agency, Inc.
31 East 10th Street
New York, N.Y. 10003

Library of Congress Catalog Card Number 64-20388

Lithographed in the U.S.A.
by Noble Offset Printers, Inc.
New York, N. Y. 10003

PREFACE

It is now over thirty years since Heaviside's operational methods of solving the differential equations of physics were first published, but hitherto they have received very little attention from mathematical physicists in general. The chief reason for this lies, I think, in the lack of a connected account of the methods. Heaviside's own work is not systematically arranged, and in places its meaning is not very clear. Bromwich's discussion of his method by means of the theory of functions of a complex variable established its validity; and as a matter of practical convenience there can be little doubt that the operational method is far the best for dealing with the class of problems concerned. It is often said that it will solve no problem that cannot be solved otherwise. Whether this is true would be difficult to say; but it is certain that in a very large class of cases the operational method will give the answer in a page when ordinary methods take five pages, and also that it gives the correct answer when the ordinary methods, through human fallibility, are liable to give a wrong one. In particular, when we discuss the small oscillations of a dynamical system with n degrees of freedom by the method of normal coordinates, we obtain a determinantal equation of the nth degree to give the speeds of the normal modes. To find the ratios of the amplitudes we must then complete the solution for each mode. If we want the actual motion due to a given initial disturbance we must solve a further family of $2n$ simultaneous equations, unless special simplifying circumstances are present. In the operational method a formal operational solution is obtained with the same amount of trouble as is needed to give the period equation in the ordinary method, and from this the complete solution is obtainable at once by a general rule of interpretation. For continuous systems the advantage of the operational method is even greater, for it gives both periods and amplitudes easily in problems where the amplitudes cannot be found by the ordinary method without a knowledge of some theorem of expansion in normal functions analogous to Fourier's theorem. Heat conduction is also especially conveniently treated by operational methods.

Since Bromwich's discussion it has often been said that the operational method is only a shorthand way of writing contour integrals. It may be;

but at least one may reply that a shorthand that avoids the necessity of writing $\frac{1}{2\pi\iota}\int_{c-\iota\infty}^{c+\iota\infty} d\lambda$ in every line of the work is worth while. Connected with the saving of writing, and perhaps largely because of it, is the fact that the operational mode of attack seems much the more natural when one has any familiarity with it. After all, the use of contour integrals in this connection was introduced by Bromwich, who has repeatedly declared that the direct operational method of solution is the better of the two.

My own reason for writing the present work is mainly that I have found Heaviside's methods useful in papers already published, and shall probably do so again soon, and I think that an accessible account of them may be equally useful to others. In one respect I must offer an apology to the reader. Heaviside developed his methods mostly in relation to the theory of electromagnetic waves. Having myself no qualification to write about electromagnetic waves I have refrained from doing so; but as the operators occurring in the theory of these waves are mostly of types treated here I think the loss will not be serious. It can in any case be remedied by reading Heaviside's works or some of the papers in the list at the end of this tract.

A chapter on dispersion has been included. The operational solution can be translated instantly into a complex integral adapted for evaluation by the method of steepest descents; a short account of the latter method has also been given, because it is not at present very accessible, and is often incorrectly believed to be more difficult than the method of stationary phase. Two cases where the Kelvin first approximation to the wave form breaks down are also discussed.

My indebtedness to the writings of Dr Bromwich is evident from the references in the text. In addition, the problems of 4.4 and 4.5 are taken directly from his lecture notes, and several others are included largely as a result of conversations with him.

My thanks are also due to the staff of the Cambridge University Press for their care and consideration during publication.

HAROLD JEFFREYS

ST JOHN'S COLLEGE,
CAMBRIDGE.

1927 *July* 19.

PREFACE TO SECOND EDITION

The chief change in this edition is the return to Heaviside's notation of p, which I had replaced by σ, for reasons that appeared to me adequate at the time. But my course was approved by nobody else, and I have not thought it worth while to maintain it. In places I have amplified the discussion, and more stress has been laid on the notion of definite integration as the fundamental operator.

The chapter on Bessel Functions has been rewritten, and a discussion of the transmission of a simple type of telegraphic signal along a cable has been added.

Thanks are due to several friends for pointing out corrections to the first edition, especially Dr S. Goldstein and Professor H. S. Carslaw.

Dr Goldstein has in addition read the whole of the present edition in proof and suggested many improvements.

My previous thanks to the staff of the Cambridge University Press must be renewed.

HAROLD JEFFREYS

1931.

AUTHOR'S NOTE

Most of the material contained in this Tract has been incorporated, corrected and amplified in *Methods of Mathematical Physics* by myself and Bertha (Swirles) Jeffreys, published by Cambridge University Press.

HAROLD JEFFREYS

1962.

CONTENTS

CHAPTER I

FUNDAMENTAL NOTIONS

1.1. Let us consider the linear differential equation of the first order

$$\frac{dy}{dx} = Ry + S, \qquad \text{.........................(1)}$$

where R and S are known functions of x, bounded and integrable when $0 \leqslant x \leqslant a$. Suppose further that $y = y_0$ when $x = 0$. Let Q denote the operation of integrating with regard to x from 0 to x, so that

$$Qy = \int_0^x y\,dx. \qquad \text{.........................(2)}$$

Perform the operation Q on both sides of the equation (1). Then we find

$$y - y_0 = Q(Ry + S), \qquad \text{.........................(3)}$$

and the right side vanishes with x. This can be rewritten in the forms

$$(1 - QR)\,y = y_0 + QS, \qquad \text{.........................(4)}$$

$$y = y_0 + QS + QRy. \qquad \text{.........................(5)}$$

These are both equivalent to the original differential equation (1) together with the given terminal condition. When we write QRy we mean, of course, that R is to be multiplied into y and the product integrated with regard to x from 0 to x. But the whole expression for y may be substituted in the last term of (5), giving in succession

$$\begin{aligned} y &= y_0 + QS + QR(y_0 + QS + QRy) \\ &= y_0 + QS + QR(y_0 + QS) + QRQR(y_0 + QS + QRy) \\ &= (y_0 + QS) + QR(y_0 + QS) + QRQR(y_0 + QS) \\ &\qquad + QRQRQR(y_0 + QS) + \dots \qquad \text{.........................(6)} \end{aligned}$$

on repeating the substitution indefinitely. We have to show that the infinite series (6) converges and that it is the correct solution. In evaluating each term R is supposed to be multiplied into the whole expression after it, and Q to operate on the whole expression after it. Suppose that within the range considered

$$|R| \leqslant A, \quad |y_0 + QS| \leqslant B, \qquad \text{.........................(7)}$$

where A and B are finite. Then the absolute value of the second term is less than ABx, that of the third than $A^2Bx^2/2!$, that of the fourth than $A^3Bx^3/3!$, while the general term is less than $A^nBx^n/n!$. Every term in the series is therefore less than the corresponding term in the series for $B \exp Ax$, and the series is therefore convergent. It therefore represents a definite function, and on substituting it in (5) we see that the equation is satisfied for all values of x; also the solution reduces to y_0 when $x=0$, as it should. Thus (6) is the correct solution.

The solution can also be written

$$y=(1+QR+QRQR+QRQRQR+\ldots)(y_0+QS). \quad \ldots\ldots(8)$$

The operator between the first pair of brackets is the binomial expansion of $(1-QR)^{-1}$, carried out as if QR was merely a number. Since y_0+QS is a determinate function, we can write the solution in the form

$$y=\frac{1}{1-QR}(y_0+QS), \quad \ldots\ldots\ldots\ldots\ldots\ldots\ldots(9)$$

provided that y_0+QS is evaluated first and that the operator $(1-QR)^{-1}$ is expanded by the binomial theorem before interpretation. In fact (9) is merely a shorthand rule for writing (8). But on returning to (4) we see that (9) is also the solution of (4) carried out as if $1-QR$ was a mere number.

It is evident from (8) that the values of S for negative values of x do not affect the solution provided y_0 is kept the same. Suppose then that S was zero for all negative values of x, and that y was zero when $x=0$. The solution would be

$$y=(1+QR+QRQR+\ldots)\,QS, \quad \ldots\ldots\ldots\ldots\ldots(10)$$

and this solution would be unaltered if the lower limits of all the integrals were replaced by $-\infty$. But if now we add to S a constant y_0/ξ for all values of x between 0 and ξ, QS will be increased by y_0 for all values of x greater than ξ, and (10) will be converted into (8). If then ξ tends to zero, y_0 remaining the same, y_ξ will tend to y_0, and we recover the solution (8) with the original initial condition. The physical interest of this result is that it corresponds to our notions of causality. Suppose that the independent variable x is the time, and that y represents the departure of some variable from its equilibrium value; then R represents a property of the system and S an external disturbing influence. If the system was originally in its equilibrium state, the form (10) exhibits the disturbance produced by the external influence after it enters. If it was undisturbed up to time zero, the part of (8) depending on S represents the effect of the finite disturbances acting at subsequent times, while the part depending on y_0 represents the effect of the impulsive disturbance at time 0 required to change y suddenly from zero to y_0. If we like we can separate the solution into two parts

$$(1-QR)^{-1}y_0 \text{ and } (1-QR)^{-1}QS,$$

and say that the first represents the effect of the initial conditions and the second that of the subsequent disturbances.

1.11. The method just given can be extended easily to cover many equations of the second and higher orders. Thus if our equation is

$$\frac{d^2y}{dx^2}=Ry+S, \qquad \text{.........................(1)}$$

with $y=y_0$ and $\dfrac{dy}{dx}=y_1$ when $x=0$, we find by integration

$$\frac{dy}{dx}-y_1=Q(Ry+S), \qquad \text{.........................(2)}$$

$$y-y_0-xy_1=QQ(Ry+S). \qquad \text{.........................(3)}$$

This leads to the solution in a series

$$y=(1+Q^2R+Q^2RQ^2R+\dots)(y_0+xy_1+Q^2S), \qquad \text{.........(4)}$$

where

$$Q^2f(x)=\int_0^x\int_0^\xi f(t)\,d\xi dt. \qquad \text{.....................(5)}$$

1.12. As a special example, consider the equation

$$\frac{dy}{dx}=ay, \qquad \text{.............................(1)}$$

with $y=1$ when $x=0$. Then carrying out the process of 1.1 (6) we get

$$y=(1+aQ+a^2Q^2+\dots)1 \qquad \text{.....................(2)}$$

$$=1+ax+\frac{a^2x^2}{2!}+\dots, \qquad \text{.........................(3)}$$

the ordinary expansion of $\exp ax$. Or take the equation

$$x\frac{d}{dx}\left(x\frac{dy}{dx}\right)+x^2y=0, \qquad \text{.........................(4)}$$

with $y=1$ and $dy/dx=0$ when $x=0$. We can infer

$$y=1-Q\left\{\frac{1}{x}Q(xy)\right\} \qquad \text{.....................................(5)}$$

$$=1-\left(\frac{x}{2}\right)^2+\frac{1}{(2!)^2}\left(\frac{x}{2}\right)^4-\frac{1}{(3!)^2}\left(\frac{x}{2}\right)^6+\dots, \qquad \text{...........(6)}$$

the ordinary expansion of $J_0(x)$.

1.2. The foregoing method is due originally to J. Caqué*; it is a valuable practical method of obtaining numerical solutions of linear differential equations. Its extension to equations of any order, or to families of simultaneous equations of the first order, is more difficult unless special simplifications enter. But if the equations have constant coefficients, which is an extremely common case in physical applications, a considerable development is possible. This arises from the fact that the operator Q obeys the fundamental laws of algebra. Thus if α is a constant and u and v are known functions of x,

$$Q(\alpha u) = \alpha(Qu), \quad \text{.....(1)}$$

$$Q(u+v) = Qu + Qv, \quad \text{.....(2)}$$

$$Q^m Q^n u = Q^n Q^m u = Q^{m+n} u. \quad \text{.....(3)}$$

Consequently Q behaves in algebraic transformations just like a number. If for instance we have two operators $f(Q)$ and $g(Q)$ both expressible as sums of integral powers of Q, thus

$$f(Q) = a_0 + a_1 Q + a_2 Q^2 + a_3 Q^3 + \ldots, \quad \text{.....(4)}$$

$$g(Q) = b_0 + b_1 Q + b_2 Q^2 + b_3 Q^3 + \ldots, \quad \text{.....(5)}$$

where the a's and b's are constants, let us for a moment replace Q by a number z small enough to make the series converge absolutely. Form the product series

$$f(z)\,g(z) = (a_0 + a_1 z + a_2 z^2 + \ldots)(b_0 + b_1 z + b_2 z^2 + \ldots)$$
$$= c_0 + c_1 z + c_2 z^2 + \ldots \quad \text{.....(6)}$$

say. Consider first the case where the series are both polynomials. Then if S is an integrable function of x

$$f(Q)\,g(Q)\,S = (c_0 + c_1 Q + c_2 Q^2 + \ldots)\,S. \quad \text{.....(7)}$$

For the left side means

$$(a_0 + a_1 Q + a_2 Q^2 + \ldots)(b_0 S + b_1 QS + b_2 Q^2 S + \ldots)$$
$$= a_0 (b_0 S + b_1 QS + b_2 Q^2 S + \ldots) + a_1 Q (b_0 S + b_1 QS + \ldots)$$
$$+ a_2 Q^2 (b_0 S + \ldots) + \ldots. \quad \text{.....(8)}$$

* *Liouville's Journal*, (2), 9 (1864), 185–222. Further developments are given by Fuchs, *Ann. d. Matem.*, (2), 4 (1870), 36–49; Peano, *Math. Ann.*, 32 (1888), 450–456; H. F. Baker, *Proc. Lond. Math. Soc.*, (1), 34 (1902), 347–360; (1), 35 (1902), 333–378; (2), 2 (1905), 293–296; *Phil. Trans.*, A, 216 (1916), 129–186. Caqué considers only a single differential equation, but notices that the operator in the result is in the form of a binomial expansion. For other operational methods based on these principles, but applicable to equations of order higher than the first, or to families of equations of the first order, the above papers of Prof. Baker may be consulted. Physical applications are given by W. L. Cowley and H. Levy, *Phil. Mag.*, 41 (1921), 584–607; Jeffreys, *Proc. Lond. Math. Soc.*, (2), 23 (1924), 454 and 465; *M.N.R.A.S.*, Geoph. Suppl. 1 (1926), 380–383.

Then using (3) we can collect the terms involving the same power of Q, and by (1) and (2) we can rearrange the series and obtain

$$a_0 b_0 S + (a_0 b_1 + a_1 b_0) QS + (a_0 b_2 + a_1 b_1 + a_2 b_0) Q^2 S + \ldots, \quad \ldots(9)$$

which is by definition the same as

$$(c_0 + c_1 Q + c_2 Q^2 + \ldots) S. \quad \ldots\ldots\ldots\ldots(10)$$

When the series are infinite, their convergence may be established easily. If the series for $f(z)$ converges absolutely when $|z| \leqslant r$, then a number M must exist such that $a_n r^n \leqslant M$ for all positive integral values of n. Thus

$$a_n \leqslant \frac{M}{r^n}, \quad \ldots\ldots\ldots\ldots(11)$$

and also if for all values of x, $|S| \leqslant C$, where C is a constant,

$$Q^n S \leqslant C \frac{x^n}{n!}. \quad \ldots\ldots\ldots\ldots(12)$$

Hence if

$$f(Q) S = \sum_{n=0}^{\infty} a_n Q^n S, \quad \ldots\ldots\ldots\ldots(13)$$

each term is less than the corresponding term of the series

$$\sum_{n=0}^{\infty} M \left(\frac{x}{r}\right)^n \frac{C}{n!}, \quad \ldots\ldots\ldots\ldots(14)$$

which converges for all values of x however large. So long as $f(z)$ is expansible about the origin in a convergent power series, however small its radius of convergence may be, the expression $f(Q) S$ will be the sum of an absolutely convergent series however great x may be. If $f(z)$ and $g(z)$ are both expansible within some circle, their product series will also converge within this circle and the expression $f(Q)\, g(Q)\, S$ will be an absolutely convergent series however great x may be. Provided with this result we can now easily extend the result (7) to the case where $f(z)$ and $g(z)$ are infinite series, by methods analogous to those used to justify the multiplication of two absolutely convergent power series.

1.3. We can now extend these methods to the solution of a family of n simultaneous differential equations of the first order with constant coefficients. Suppose that the equations are

$$\left.\begin{array}{l} e_{11} x_1 + e_{12} x_2 + \ldots + e_{1n} x_n = S_1 \\ e_{21} x_1 + e_{22} x_2 + \ldots + e_{2n} x_n = S_2 \\ \ldots\ldots\ldots\ldots\ldots\ldots\ldots\ldots \\ e_{n1} x_1 + e_{n2} x_2 + \ldots + e_{nn} x_n = S_n \end{array}\right\}, \quad \ldots\ldots\ldots\ldots(1)$$

where the x's are the dependent variables, the independent variable is t, and e_{rs} denotes $a_{rs}\frac{d}{dt}+b_{rs}$, where a_{rs} and b_{rs} are constants; the S's are known functions of t. We do not assume that

$$a_{rs}=a_{sr}, \qquad b_{rs}=b_{sr},$$

but we do assume that the determinant formed by the a_{rs} is not zero. The terminal conditions are that when $t=0$, $x_1=u_1$ and so on, where the u's are known constants.

The typical equation (1) can be written shortly

$$\Sigma_s e_{rs}x_s=S_r \qquad (s=1,\ 2,\ \ldots\ n) \quad \text{.................(2)}$$

or, using the convention familiar in tensor calculus, that a repeated suffix such as s is to be given all possible values and the results added, simply

$$e_{rs}x_s=S_r. \quad \text{..............................(3)}$$

First perform the operation of definite integration with regard to t from 0 to t on both sides of this equation. We have

$$\begin{aligned} Qe_{rs}x_s &= \int_0^t \left(a_{rs}\frac{dx_s}{dt}+b_{rs}x_s\right)dt \\ &= a_{rs}(x_s-u_s)+b_{rs}Qx_s \\ &= f_{rs}x_s-a_{rs}u_s, \quad \text{..........................(4)} \end{aligned}$$

where f_{rs} denotes the operator $a_{rs}+b_{rs}Q$. Then the original equations and the initial conditions together are equivalent to the n equations

$$f_{rs}x_s=v_r+QS_r, \quad \text{..........................(5)}$$

where

$$v_r=a_{rs}u_s. \quad \text{..............................(6)}$$

Now let D denote the operational determinant formed by the f_{rs}, namely

$$||f_{rs}||=\begin{vmatrix} f_{11} & f_{12} & \cdots & f_{1n} \\ f_{21} & f_{22} & \cdots & f_{2n} \\ \cdots & \cdots & \cdots & \cdots \\ f_{n1} & f_{n2} & \cdots & f_{nn} \end{vmatrix}. \quad \text{.................(7)}$$

If this determinant is expanded by the ordinary rules of algebra and equal powers of Q are collected, we obtain a polynomial in Q, ordinarily of degree n. The term independent of Q is simply the determinant $||a_{rs}||$, which by hypothesis does not vanish. Now let F_{rs} denote the minor of f_{rs} in this determinant, taken with its proper sign. F_{rs} is a polynomial in Q, ordinarily of degree $n-1$.

Now operate on the first of (5) with F_{1m}, on the second with F_{2m}, and so on, and add. Then

$$F_{rm} f_{rs} x_s = F_{rm} (v_r + QS_r), \quad \text{......................(8)}$$

where summation with regard to s is understood on the left, and with regard to r on both sides. The operator acting on a particular x_s is $F_{rm} f_{rs} (r = 1, 2, \ldots n)$. If $s = m$, this is equal to the determinant D; if $s \neq m$, it is a determinant with two columns equal and therefore is zero. Hence (8) is equivalent to

$$D x_m = F_{rm} (v_r + QS_r). \quad \text{........................(9)}$$

Now if all the S_r are integrable within the range of values of t contemplated, the expression on the right of (9) is also integrable. Also since the function $D(z)$, obtained by replacing Q in D by a number z, is regular and not zero at $z = 0$, the function $1/D(z)$ is expressible as a power series in z with a finite radius of convergence. Define D^{-1} as the power series in Q obtained by putting Q for z in the series for $1/D(z)$. Then operate on both sides of (9) with D^{-1}. We have

$$D^{-1} D x_m = D^{-1} F_{rm} (v_r + QS_r). \quad \text{..............(10)}$$

But, since series of positive integral powers of Q can be multiplied according to the rules of algebra, $D^{-1} D$ gives simply unity, and we have the solution

$$x_m = D^{-1} F_{rm} (v_r + QS_r). \quad \text{.....................(11)}$$

This gives a complete formal solution of the problem. Its form is often convenient for actual computation, especially for small values of t; but it can also be expressed in finite terms. For the v_r are constants, and (11) is therefore of the form

$$x_m = \frac{\phi_m(Q)}{D(Q)} + \frac{F_{rm}}{D(Q)} QS_r, \quad \text{.................(12)}$$

where ϕ_m and F_{rm} are polynomials, usually of degree one less than D. Since the determinant $||a_{rs}||$ is not zero we may denote it by A, and D is the product of n linear factors, thus

$$D = A (1 - \alpha_1 Q)(1 - \alpha_2 Q) \ldots (1 - \alpha_n Q), \quad \text{...........(13)}$$

where the α's will ordinarily be all different. Then $\phi_m(Q)/D(Q)$ can be expressed as the sum of a number of partial fractions of the form

$$\frac{L}{1 - \alpha Q}. \quad \text{............................(14)}$$

But by 1.12 (3) this is the same as $Le^{\alpha t}$. The part of the solution arising from the v's can therefore be expressed as a linear combination of exponentials.

The justification of this decomposition into partial fractions is that it is a purely algebraic process. Hence if the partial fractions and the original operator are all expanded in positive powers of Q, and like powers of Q are collected, the coefficients of a given power of Q will be the same in both expansions, and the equivalence is complete.

Exceptional cases will occur if D contains no term in Q^n, or if two or more of the α's are equal. If the term in Q^n is absent the expansion of the operator in partial fractions will usually contain a constant term. If the term in Q^{n-1} is also absent we must divide out, and the expansion in partial fractions will contain a term in Q; this will give a term in t on interpretation.

If several of the α's are equal, the expression in partial fractions will involve terms of the form $M(1-\alpha Q)^{-r}$. These can be interpreted by direct expansion; but another method is more convenient. Starting with

$$(1-\alpha Q)^{-1}=e^{\alpha t}, \qquad \text{.........................(15)}$$

let us differentiate $r-1$ times with regard to α. We find

$$\frac{(r-1)!\,Q^{r-1}}{(1-\alpha Q)^r}=t^{r-1}e^{\alpha t}, \qquad \text{.......................(16)}$$

so that

$$\frac{Q^{r-1}}{(1-\alpha Q)^r}=\frac{t^{r-1}}{(r-1)!}e^{\alpha t}. \qquad \text{....................(17)}$$

A rather different form of resolution into partial fractions from the ordinary one is therefore necessary if each fraction is to give a single term in the solution. Instead of having constants in all the numerators we must have powers of Q, the power of Q needed in any fraction being one less than the degree of the denominator. But if we write p^{-1} for Q the fraction in (16) is algebraically equivalent to $p/(p-\alpha)^r$. In this form the power of p in the numerator is independent of the degree of the denominator, and it is easier to resolve into partial fractions of this form than into those involving Q directly.

The above remarks apply to the interpretation of the effect of the initial conditions; that is, of the first term on the right of (11). To find the effect of the terms in the S's we may expand the operators similarly. To interpret $(1-\alpha Q)^{-1}QS$ in finite terms, we note that it is the solution of $\frac{dy}{dt}-\alpha y=S$ that vanishes with t. This is easily found by the ordinary method to be

$$y=e^{\alpha t}Q\,(Se^{-\alpha t}), \qquad \text{.......................(18)}$$

which is the interpretation required.

To sum up, we can solve a family of equations of the type (1) by first integrating each equation once from 0 to t with regard to t, allowing for the initial conditions. This gives a set of equations of the type (3). The subsequent process for deducing the operational solution (10) is exactly the same as if the operators f_{rs} were numbers, and the ordinary rules of algebra were applied. The solution can be evaluated by expanding the operators in ascending powers of Q and evaluating term by term; this in general gives an infinite series. Alternatively it can be obtained by resolving into partial fractions and interpreting each fraction separately; this gives an explicit solution in finite terms.

1.4. Heaviside's method is equivalent to that just given; it differs in using another notation, which is not quite so convenient in a formal proof of the theorem, but is rather more convenient for actual application. In Heaviside's notation the operator above called Q is denoted by p^{-1}. At present we need not specify the meaning of positive powers of p; negative integral powers are defined by induction, so that p^{-n} denotes Q^n. We have noticed that the passage from 1.3 (5) to 1.3 (11) is a purely algebraic process. Consequently if all the equations 1.3 (5) were multiplied by constants before the algebraic solution the same answer would be obtained. Suppose then that we write the general equation 1.3 (5) in the form

$$(a_{rs} + b_{rs}p^{-1})\, x_s = a_{rs} u_s + p^{-1} S_r. \qquad \text{..................(1)}$$

Multiply throughout by p as if this was a constant. We get

$$(a_{rs} p + b_{rs})\, x_s = a_{rs}\, p u_s + S_r. \qquad \text{..................(2)}$$

On solving the n equations of this form we shall obtain a solution identical with 1.3 (11) except that p^{-1} will appear for Q, and both numerator and denominator will be multiplied by the same power of p. If the operators in the solution are expanded in negative powers of p, and p^{-1} is then interpreted as Q, the result will be identical with that already given. Comparing (2) with the original equations 1.3 (1) we see that the new form of our rule is as follows:

Write p for d/dt on the left of each equation; to the right of each equation add the result of dropping the b's on the left and replacing the x's by their initial values; solve the resulting equations (2) by algebra as if p was a number; and evaluate the result by expanding in negative powers of p and interpreting p^{-1} as the operation of integrating from 0 to t.

This is Heaviside's rule. In what follows the equations (2) will usually be called the subsidiary equations.

To obtain the solution explicitly, we put e_{rs} for $a_{rs}p+b_{rs}$, denote our determinant

$$\begin{vmatrix} e_{11} & e_{12} & \cdots & e_{1n} \\ e_{21} & e_{22} & \cdots & e_{2n} \\ \cdots & \cdots & \cdots & \cdots \\ e_{n1} & e_{n2} & \cdots & e_{nn} \end{vmatrix}$$

by Δ, and denote the minor of e_{rs} in this determinant, taken with its proper sign, by E_{rs}. Then the solution is

$$x_m = \frac{E_{rm}}{\Delta}(pa_{rs}u_s + S_r). \quad \text{.......................(3)}$$

Since the determinant formed by the a's is not zero, Δ is of degree n in p, while E_{rm} is at most of degree $n-1$. The operators can therefore be expanded in negative powers of p, as we should expect; positive powers do not occur. All terms after the first vanish with t; the first is

$$\frac{A_{rm}}{A} a_{rs}u_s, \quad \text{...............................(4)}$$

where A_{rs} is the minor of a_{rs} in A. But

$$\left.\begin{aligned} A_{rm}a_{rs} &= A \ (m=s) \\ &= 0 \ (m \neq s) \end{aligned}\right\}, \quad \text{.......................(5)}$$

and (4) reduces to u_m, as we should expect. This verifies that the solution satisfies the initial conditions.

1.5. To interpret the operational solution 1.4 (3) in finite terms we require rules for interpreting rational functions of p operating on unity and on other functions. We have already had the rules

$$p^{-1} = Q; \ p^{-2} = Q^2; \ \text{and so on}, \quad \text{..................(1)}$$

$$p^{-1}1 = Q1 = t; \ p^{-2}1 = Qt = \frac{t^2}{2!}; \ \text{and in general } p^{-n}1 = \frac{t^n}{n!}. \quad \text{...(2)}$$

If unity is replaced by Heaviside's 'unit function,' here denoted by $H(t)$, which is zero for all negative values of t and 1 for all positive values, we still have

$$p^{-n}H(t) = \frac{t^n}{n!}, \quad \text{........................(3)}$$

when t is positive, but it will vanish when t is negative. We can also replace the lower limit of the integrations by $-\infty$ or by any negative constant without altering this interpretation.

Again, we shall have when t is positive

$$\frac{p}{p-\alpha}=\frac{1}{1-\alpha Q}=e^{\alpha t}, \quad\text{..........................(4)}$$

$$\frac{p}{(p-\alpha)^n}=\frac{Q^{n-1}}{(1-\alpha Q)^n}=\frac{t^{n-1}}{(n-1)!}e^{\alpha t}, \quad\text{..............(5)}$$

$$\frac{\alpha}{p-\alpha}=\frac{p}{p-\alpha}-1=e^{\alpha t}-1, \quad\text{.................(6)}$$

where the function operated on may be either unity or $H(t)$. In the latter case all the operators will give zero for negative values of t.

The operators in 1.4 (3) are of the form $f(p)/F(p)$, where $f(p)$ and $F(p)$ are polynomials in p, and $f(p)$ is of the same or lower degree than $F(p)$. If $F(p)$ is of degree n it can be resolved into n linear factors of the form $p-\alpha$. Then provided that the α's are all different and none of them zero we have the algebraic identity

$$\frac{f(p)}{pF(p)}=\frac{f(0)}{pF(0)}+\Sigma_\alpha \frac{f(\alpha)}{\alpha F'(\alpha)}\frac{1}{p-\alpha}, \quad\text{...........(7)}$$

whence

$$\frac{f(p)}{F(p)}=\frac{f(0)}{F(0)}+\Sigma_\alpha \frac{f(\alpha)}{\alpha F'(\alpha)}\frac{p}{p-\alpha}. \quad\text{...........(8)}$$

If this operates on unity or $H(t)$ we have therefore for positive values of t

$$\frac{f(p)}{F(p)}1=\frac{f(0)}{F(0)}+\Sigma_\alpha \frac{f(\alpha)}{\alpha F'(\alpha)}e^{\alpha t}. \quad\text{.................(9)}$$

To justify this we notice as before that (8) is a purely algebraic identity, and therefore if both sides are expanded in negative powers of p, beginning with constant terms, the expansion of the two sides will be identical, and on interpretation in terms of integrations will give the same result.

The formula (9) is usually known as Heaviside's expansion theorem; but as Heaviside's methods involve two other expansion theorems* it will be called the 'partial-fraction rule' in the present work.

If some of the α's are equal or zero, the expression (7) considered as a function of p will have a multiple pole, and its expression in partial fractions will contain terms of the form $(p-\alpha)^{-s}$, where s is an integer greater than unity, and α may be zero. Then $f(p)/F(p)$ will contain terms of the forms $p^{-(s-1)}$ or $p/(p-\alpha)^s$, which can be interpreted by means of (2) or (5).

* Namely, expansion in powers of Q or p^{-1} and interpretation term by term; and expansion in powers of e^{-ph}, where h is a constant, as in 4.2.

By means of these rules we can evaluate all the expressions for the part of x_m in 1.4 (3) that depends on the initial values of the x's. If the S's are constant for positive values of t, as they often are, the same rules will apply to the part of the solution depending on them. If they are exponential functions such as $e^{\mu t}$, the easiest plan is usually to rewrite this as $p/(p-\mu)$ and reinterpret. Thus

$$\frac{f(p)}{F(p)}e^{\mu t}=\frac{f(p)}{F(p)}\frac{p}{p-\mu} \qquad (10)$$

$$=\frac{f(\mu)}{F(\mu)}e^{\mu t}+\Sigma\frac{f(\alpha)}{(\alpha-\mu)F'(\alpha)}e^{\alpha t}. \qquad (11)$$

If S is expressed as a linear combination of exponentials we can apply this rule to each separately. This is applicable to practically all functions known to physics.

Alternatively we can resolve the operator acting on S into partial fractions and interpret $p^{-n}S$ by integration and other fractions by the rule 1.3 (18)

$$\frac{1}{p-\alpha}S=e^{\alpha t}\int_0^t Se^{-\alpha t}dt. \qquad (12)$$

This completes our rules for solving a set of linear equations of the first order with constant coefficients. In comparison with the ordinary method, we notice that the rules are direct and lead immediately to a solution involving operators, which can then be evaluated completely by known rules. If it happens that we only require the variation of one unknown explicitly, we need not interpret the solutions for the others. In the ordinary method we have to find a complementary function and a particular integral separately. To find the former we assume a solution of the form $x_s=\lambda_s e^{\alpha t}$ and on substituting in the differential equations with the S's omitted we find an equation of consistency to determine the n possible values of α, and the ratios of the λ's corresponding to each. The particular integral is then found by some method, but it does not as a rule vanish with t. The actual values of the λ's are still undetermined, and the value associated with each α must be found by substituting in the initial conditions and again solving a set of n simultaneous equations. The labour of finding the equation for the α's and the ratios of the λ's corresponding to one of them is about the same as that of finding the operational solution of Heaviside's method; the rest of the work is avoided by the operational method. Further, if some of the α's are equal or zero considerable complications are introduced into the ordinary method, but not into the operational one.

1.6. The above work is applicable to all cases where A is not zero. If it is zero, we can show that there is some defect in the specification of the system. A system is adequately specified if when we know the values of the dependent variables and the external disturbances at any instant the rates of change of the dependent variables are all determinate. Now if A is zero, let us multiply the rth equation

$$\left(a_{rs}\frac{dx_s}{dt}+b_{rs}\right)x_s=S_r \qquad \text{.......................(1)}$$

by A_{rm}, the minor of a_{rm} in A, and add. Then

$$A_{rm}\,a_{rs}\frac{dx_s}{dt}=A_{rm}\,(S_r-b_{rs}x_s). \qquad \text{..................(2)}$$

The coefficient of dx_s/dt on the left is $A_{rm}a_{rs}$. If $s\neq m$, this is a determinant with two columns equal, and is therefore zero; if $s=m$, it is equal to A, and is again zero. Thus the left side vanishes identically, and the x's are permanently connected by the relation

$$A_{rm}\,(b_{rs}x_s-S_r)=0. \qquad \text{.......................(3)}$$

If the coefficients $A_{rm}b_{rs}$ vanish, there must be a permanent relation between the S_r, and one of the original equations is a mere logical consequence of the others; then we have not enough equations to determine the derivatives. If they do not vanish, the values of the x_s when $t=0$ are connected by a definite relation, so that the initial values of the x_s cannot be assigned independently.

1.7. The method is most easily extended to equations of higher order by breaking them up into equations of the first order. Thus if we have an equation of the second order such as

$$\frac{d^2x}{dt^2}+a\frac{dx}{dt}+bx=S, \qquad \text{.......................(1)}$$

we introduce a new variable y given by

$$\frac{dx}{dt}-y=0, \qquad \text{...........................(2)}$$

and the original equation can be replaced by

$$\frac{dy}{dt}+ay+bx=S. \qquad \text{..........................(3)}$$

We have now two equations of the first order in x and y. If initially $x=x_0$ and $dx/dt=x_1$, the subsidiary equations are

$$px-y=px_0, \qquad \text{.........................(4)}$$

$$(p+a)\,y+bx=px_1+S. \qquad \text{....................(5)}$$

Solving by algebra we find

$$x = \frac{(p^2 + ap)\,x_0 + px_1 + S}{p^2 + ap + b}. \quad \text{......................(6)}$$

To interpret, put

$$p^2 + ap + b = (p - \alpha)(p - \beta), \quad \text{..................(7)}$$

and apply the partial-fraction rule. We find

$$x = \frac{1}{\alpha - \beta}(x_1 - \beta x_0)\,e^{\alpha t} - \frac{1}{\alpha - \beta}(x_1 - \alpha x_0)\,e^{\beta t}$$

$$+ \frac{1}{\alpha - \beta}\left[e^{\alpha t}\int_0^t Se^{-\alpha t}\,dt - e^{\beta t}\int_0^t Se^{-\beta t}\,dt\right], \quad \text{...(8)}$$

which is easily shown to satisfy all the conditions and therefore to be the solution required.

1.71. A few illustrative examples may be given. (p is written for d/dt from the start.)

1. $$(p^2 + 4p + 3)\,x = 1;\ x_0 = 3;\ x_1 = -2.$$

We consider the subsidiary equation

$$(p^2 + 4p + 3)\,x = 1 - 2p + 3\,(p^2 + 4p)$$
$$= 3p^2 + 10p + 1.$$

Then $$x = \frac{3p^2 + 10p + 1}{(p+1)(p+3)}$$
$$= \tfrac{1}{3} + 3e^{-t} - \tfrac{1}{3}e^{-3t},$$

on interpreting by the partial-fraction rule.

2. $$(p^2 + 5p + 6)\,x = 12;\ x_0 = 2;\ x_1 = 0.$$

Consider $$(p^2 + 5p + 6)\,x = 12 + 2\,(p^2 + 5p).$$

Cancelling the common factor,

$$x = 2.$$

3. $$(p + 3)\,x = e^{-2t};\ y_0 = 0.$$

This can be written $$(p + 3)\,x = \frac{p}{p + 2};$$

or $$x = \frac{p}{(p + 2)(p + 3)}$$
$$= e^{-2t} - e^{-3t}.$$

4. $$(p^2 + n^2)\,x = 0.$$

Here $$x = \frac{p^2 x_0 + p x_1}{p^2 + n^2} = x_0 \cos nt + x_1 \frac{\sin nt}{n}.$$

5. $(p+2)^2 x = t^2 e^{-2t};\ x_0 = 0;\ x_1 = 0.$

The expression on the right is equivalent to the operator $2p/(p+2)^3$. Hence

$$x = \frac{2p}{(p+2)^5} = \frac{2t^4}{4!} e^{-2t} = \frac{1}{12} t^4 e^{-2t}.$$

We notice the advantage of Heaviside's method in avoiding the use of simultaneous equations to determine the so-called 'arbitrary' constants of the ordinary method. In particular in the second example the data have a property leading to a simple solution. Heaviside's method seizes upon this immediately and gives the solution in one line; with the ordinary method the simultaneous equations for the constants would have to be solved as usual.

In general we may say that the more specific the problem the greater will be the convenience of the operational method.

1.72. The method just given can be extended easily to a family of equations of the second order. If the typical equation is again written

$$e_{rs} x_s = S_r, \quad \text{.............................(1)}$$

where now

$$e_{rs} = a_{rs} \frac{d^2}{dt^2} + b_{rs} \frac{d}{dt} + c_{rs}, \quad \text{....................(2)}$$

we can introduce n new variables $y_1, y_2, \dots y_n$ given by

$$\frac{dx_s}{dt} - y_s = 0, \quad \text{.............................(3)}$$

thus treating the first derivatives of the x's as a set of new variables. Then the equations (1) are equivalent to

$$a_{rs} \frac{dy_s}{dt} + (b_{rs} y_s + c_{rs} x_s) = S_r, \quad \text{....................(4)}$$

and (3) and (4) constitute a set of $2n$ equations of the first order. Suppose also that when $t=0$, $x_s = u_s$, $y_s = v_s$. According to our rule of 1.5 we must replace d/dt by p and add pu_s to the right of (3), and $a_{rs} pv_s$ to the right of (4). We have now to solve by algebra, and may begin by writing the revised form of (3)

$$y_s = p(x_s - u_s). \quad \text{..........................(5)}$$

When we substitute in the modified form of (4) we get

$$a_{rs} p^2 (x_s - u_s) + b_{rs} p (x_s - u_s) + c_{rs} x_s = S_r + a_{rs} pv_s, \quad \text{........(6)}$$

or, on rearranging,

$$(a_{rs} p^2 + b_{rs} p + c_{rs}) x_s = (a_{rs} p^2 + b_{rs} p) u_s + a_{rs} pv_s + S_r. \quad \text{......(7)}$$

We have thus n equations for the x's to solve by algebra, and the solution can be interpreted by the rules.

In Bromwich's paper 'Normal Coordinates in Dynamical Systems' a method equivalent to the operational one is applied directly to a set of second order equations. First order equations, however, arise in some problems of physical interest, and merit a direct discussion. This, as we have seen, is easily generalized to equations of the second order.

1.8. In all the problems considered so far the operators that occur in the solutions are expansible in positive powers of Q, or in negative powers of p, and we have seen that so long as the series obtained by replacing Q by a number have a finite radius of convergence, however small, the operational solution is intelligible in terms of the definitions we have had. But we have not defined p as such, because we have only needed to define its negative powers, and p cannot be expanded in terms of its own negative powers. Then has p any meaning of its own? Since it replaces d/dt when we form the subsidiary equation we may naturally suppose that p means d/dt, and this is the meaning sometimes actually attributed to it; but care is needed. We recall that when the subsidiary equation is formed a term like px_0 appears on the right; but dx_0/dt is zero, so that if we pushed this interpretation too far we should be faced with the alarming result that the solutions of the equations do not depend on their initial values. The fact is that though the operators d/dt and Q both satisfy the laws of algebra and are freely commutative with constants, they are not as a rule commutative with each other. Thus

$$\frac{d}{dt} Qf(t) = \frac{d}{dt}\int_0^t f(t)\,dt = f(t), \quad \text{..................(1)}$$

$$Q\frac{d}{dt} f(t) = \int_0^t f'(t)\,dt = f(t) - f(0). \quad \text{...........(2)}$$

Thus the operators p and Q are commutative if, and only if, the function operated on vanishes with t. It appears from (1) that d/dt undoes the operation Q if d/dt acts after Q. With this convention we can identify p, the inverse of Q, with d/dt. When p and Q both occur in an operator, the Q operations must be carried out before the differentiations*.

My own view is that the method of expansion in positive powers of D, which is given in text-books of differential equations for finding particular integrals, should be abandoned because it leads to intelligible results only in two very special cases, and should be replaced by the

* Cf. Heaviside, *Electromagnetic Theory*, 2, 298.

present one. The treatment of such equations by the present method is as follows. Suppose that the differential equation is

$$\phi\left(\frac{d}{dt}\right) y = \frac{d^n y}{dt^n} + a_1 \frac{d^{n-1} y}{dt^{n-1}} + \dots + a_n y = f(t),$$

where $f(t)$ is known, and that when $t = 0$

$$y = y_0; \quad \frac{dy}{dt} = y_1; \quad \dots \quad \frac{d^{n-1} y}{dt^{n-1}} = y_{n-1}.$$

We integrate n times from 0 to t, determining the constant of integration at each stage. The resulting equation is

$$\begin{aligned} 1 + a_1 Qy + \dots + a_n Q^n y = {} & (1 + a_1 Q + \dots + a_{n-1} Q^{n-1}) y_0 \\ & + (Q + a_1 Q^2 + \dots + a_{n-2} Q^{n-1}) y_1 \\ & + \dots\dots\dots\dots\dots\dots \\ & + Q^{n-1} y_{n-1} + Q^n f(t). \end{aligned}$$

We write Q as p^{-1} and write the subsidiary equation as

$$\begin{aligned} \phi(p) y = (p^n + a_1 p^{n-1} + \dots + a_n) y = {} & (p^n + a_1 p^{n-1} + \dots + a_{n-1} p) y_0 \\ & + (p^{n-1} + a_1 p^{n-2} + \dots + a_{n-2} p) y_1 \\ & + \dots\dots\dots\dots\dots\dots \\ & + p y_{n-1} + f(t) \\ & = g(p) + f(t) \end{aligned}$$

say. Then the operational solution is

$$y = \frac{g(p)}{\phi(p)} + \frac{1}{\phi(p)} f(t).$$

The first part expresses the effect of the initial conditions, and in the usual nomenclature gives the complementary function. The part depending on $f(t)$ gives a particular integral, which can always be obtained formally by 1.5 (12).

The text-book method (due to Boole) is applicable if $f(t)$ is a polynomial, or if it is expressible in the form $e^{\mu t} F(t)$, where $F(t)$ is a polynomial. Suppose first that our solution is

$$y = \frac{1}{\phi(p)} t^m,$$

where m is an integer. We write this as

$$y = \frac{m!}{\phi(p) p^m} = \frac{m!}{(p - \alpha_1)(p - \alpha_2) \dots (p - \alpha_n) p^m}.$$

The operator must be broken up into partial fractions. If all the α's are distinct and different from zero, the fractions arising from them are

$$\Sigma_\alpha \frac{m!\, p}{\alpha^{m+1} \phi'(\alpha)(p - \alpha)} = \Sigma_\alpha \frac{m!}{\alpha^{m+1} \phi'(\alpha)} e^{\alpha t},$$

which would in Boole's treatment be part of the complementary function. The contribution from the part near $p = 0$ is to be found by expanding

$$Y_0 = \frac{m!}{p^m} \cdot \frac{1}{\phi(p)}$$

in *ascending* powers of p until we reach a constant term. Then

$$\begin{aligned} Y_0 = \frac{m!}{p^m} \frac{1}{a_n + a_{n-1}p + \dots} &= \frac{m!}{a_n}\left(p^{-m} - \frac{a_{n-1}p_1^{-m+1}}{a_n} + \dots\right) \\ &= \frac{m!}{a_n}\left(\frac{t^m}{m!} - \frac{a_{n-1}}{a_n}\frac{t^{m-1}}{(m-1)!} + \dots\right) \\ &= \frac{t^m}{a_n} - \frac{a_{n-1} m t^{m-1}}{a_n^2} + \dots, \end{aligned}$$

taken as far as the constant term. But this is precisely the result given by Boole's method when we expand $1/\phi(D)$ in ascending powers of D as far as D^m and make it operate on t^m. To this extent therefore the methods are equivalent; but Heaviside's method gives the integral that vanishes with its first $n-1$ derivatives at $t = 0$, while Boole's leaves the coefficients of the exponentials to be determined separately.

Now consider the function $p^{-1}[e^{at}F(t)]$, where $F(t)$ is a known integrable function. We have

$$\begin{aligned} p^{-1}[e^{at}F(t)] = \int_0^t e^{at}F(t)\,dt &= \int_0^t e^{at} d\{p^{-1}F(t)\} \\ &= \left[e^{at}p^{-1}F(t)\right]_0^t - \mu\int_0^t e^{at}p^{-1}F(t)\,dt \\ &= e^{at}[p^{-1} - ap^{-2} + a^2p^{-3} - \dots]F(t), \end{aligned}$$

all integrals vanishing at $t = 0$ since $F(t)$ is integrable. Thus

$$p^{-1}[e^{at}F(t)] = e^{at}\frac{1}{p+a}F(t).$$

Repeating the process, we have

$$p^{-m}[e^{at}F(t)] = e^{at}\frac{1}{(p+a)^m}F(t),$$

and therefore, if $1/\phi(p)$ is expansible in negative powers of p,

$$\frac{1}{\phi(p)}e^{at}F(t) = e^{at}\frac{1}{\phi(p+a)}F(t).$$

This replaces the corresponding theorem in the ordinary treatment.

This result explains why some of our interpretations differ from those given in text-books of differential equations for the determination of particular integrals. For instance, we have interpreted $1/(p-a)$ as $\frac{1}{a}(e^{at}-1)$. In the ordinary method, we expand this operator in ascending powers of p and then interpret p as d/dt. Thus

$$\frac{1}{p-a}1=-\left(\frac{1}{a}+\frac{p}{a^2}+\dots\right)1=-\frac{1}{a}. \quad \dots\dots\dots\dots\dots(3)$$

This assumes that the sum of all the terms on the right after the first is zero. But

$$\left(\frac{1}{p-a}+\frac{1}{a}\right)1=\frac{p}{a(p-a)}1. \quad \dots\dots\dots\dots\dots(4)$$

By our rules we should interpret the function on the right as $\frac{1}{a}e^{at}$. If we write it as $\frac{1}{a}.p.\frac{1}{p-a}.1$ and interpret the first p as d/dt, it gives

$$\frac{1}{a}.p.\frac{1}{p-a}.1=\frac{1}{a}\frac{d}{dt}\left\{\frac{1}{a}(e^{at}-1)\right\}=\frac{1}{a}e^{at}, \quad \dots\dots\dots(5)$$

agreeing with the former interpretation. But if we write it as $\frac{1}{a}.\frac{1}{p-a}.p.1$ and interpret the p as meaning d/dt, it is clearly zero. The difference arises from the fact that the operators d/dt and $(p-a)^{-1}$ are non-commutative; the right result is the one obtained by operating with $(p-a)^{-1}$ *first*.

We may notice, incidentally, that whereas the series in powers of Q always give convergent series on interpretation, the same is not true of the corresponding series in powers of d/dt. For instance, if $S=t^r$, where r is fractional, the series for $\frac{1}{p-1}.S$ in ascending powers of p diverges like $\Sigma t^{-n}n!$. Apart from the greater internal consistency of Heaviside's methods, then, they are capable of much wider application.

1.9. An interpretation of the operator e^{hp} is suggested by Heaviside, as follows:

$$e^{hp}f(t)=\left(1+hp+\frac{h^2p^2}{2!}+\dots\right)f(t)$$

$$=f(t)+hf'(t)+\frac{h^2}{2!}f''(t)+\dots$$

$$=f(t+h) \quad \dots\dots\dots\dots\dots\dots\dots\dots(6)$$

by Taylor's theorem, if we interpret p as d/dt. The operator then increases the argument of the function by h. But this is clearly dangerous; for suppose that $f(t)$ is 0 for $-1<t<1$, and equal to t^2-1 for t outside these limits. If in the series on the right we put $t=0$, every term vanishes, and apparently for *all* values of h

$$f(h)=f(0)+hf'(0)+\dots$$
$$=0. \qquad \text{.........(7)}$$

But $f(h)$ is not zero if $|h|$ exceeds 1. The fact is, of course, that Taylor's theorem is not applicable to a function of this type, but only to functions expressible by a single power series throughout their range of existence. It actually appears, however, as we shall see later, that the formula (6) is more general than Taylor's theorem and that its justification does not depend on the interpretation of p as d/dt. At present we may simply take it as the *definition* of the operator; we *define* $e^{hp}f(t)$ to mean $f(t+h)$. We must now examine whether this operator commutes with Q and with d/dt. We have

$$e^{hp}Qf(t)=e^{hp}\int_0^t f(t)\,dt=\int_0^{t+h} f(t)\,dt, \qquad \text{.........(8)}$$

$$Qe^{hp}f(t)=Qf(t+h)=\int_0^t f(t+h)\,dt=\int_h^{t+h} f(t)\,dt, \qquad \text{...(9)}$$

so that the operators e^{hp} and Q are commutative if $\int_0^h f(t)\,dt=0$. This restriction is less serious than might appear, because many of our functions vanish for *all* negative values of t. Then if h is negative the condition is satisfied.

Also
$$e^{hp}\frac{d}{dt}f(t)=e^{hp}f'(t)=f'(t+h), \qquad \text{.........(10)}$$

$$\frac{d}{dt}e^{hp}f(t)=\frac{d}{dt}f(t+h)=f'(t+h), \qquad \text{.........(11)}$$

so that e^{hp} and d/dt are always commutative.

The operator e^{hp} is useful in enabling us to find a theorem that plays in Heaviside's method a part closely analogous to that played by Fourier's integral theorem in the ordinary method. Instead of treating trigonometric functions as fundamental, Heaviside uses his 'unit function,' here called $H(t)$, which is unity for positive and zero for negative values of t. Then

$$e^{hp}H(t)=H(t+h) \qquad \text{.........(12)}$$

and is equal to 1 if $t>-h$ and to 0 if $t<-h$. Then if $h_1<h_2$,

$$(e^{-ph_1}-e^{-ph_2})\,H(t)=H(t-h_1)-H(t-h_2)$$
$$\left.\begin{aligned}&=1 \text{ if } h_1<t<h_2\\ &=0 \text{ if } t<h_1\\ \text{and } &=0 \text{ if } t>h_2\end{aligned}\right\}. \qquad \text{.........(13)}$$

If, further, $h_1 < h_2 < h_3 < \ldots < h_n$,

$$\{(e^{-ph_1} - e^{-ph_2}) f(h_1) + (e^{-ph_2} - e^{-ph_3}) f(h_2) + \ldots + (e^{-ph_{n-1}} - e^{-ph_n}) f(h_{n-1})\} H(t)$$
$$= 0 \text{ for } t < h_1, f(h_1) \text{ for } h_1 < t < h_2, \text{ and so on.} \quad \ldots(14)$$

If then the subdivisions of the interval h_1 to h_n become indefinitely numerous and close, we can approximate as closely as we like to a function $f(t)$ by a sum $\Sigma f(h_r)(e^{-ph_r} - e^{-ph_{r+1}}) H(t)$. In the limit we can replace this sum by an integral and write

$$f(t) = -\int_{h=-\infty}^{\infty} f(h)\, d[e^{-ph} H(t)]. \quad \ldots\ldots\ldots\ldots(15)$$

The function under the d sign being discontinuous at $h = t$, the integral is of Stieltjes type*, and its meaning is really defined as the limit of (14). But we can often formally integrate with regard to h as if p was a number, and obtain a function of p operating on $H(t)$. In this way a given function of t can be expressed in the operational form, thus

$$f(t) = g(p) H(t). \quad \ldots\ldots\ldots\ldots\ldots\ldots\ldots\ldots(16)$$

This device often simplifies the evaluation of the result of an operation on a function; for if our solution is $\phi(p) f(t)$, say, we can interpret it as $\phi(p) g(p) H(t)$, and then interpret directly the result of operating on $H(t)$ with $\phi(p) g(p)$.

If in the equations 1.3 (1) all the S's are zero except one, and that one is $H(t)$, it gives a contribution to any coordinate of the form

$$x = \phi(p) H(t). \quad \ldots\ldots\ldots\ldots\ldots\ldots\ldots\ldots(17)$$

Suppose now that we replace $H(t)$ by $H(t-h)$. The corresponding contribution to the solution is $\phi(p) H(t-h)$. We can now extend (17) to a general S, for if, as in (14), $S = f(h_r)$ from $t = h_r$ to h_{r+1}, we can write the contribution to the solution

$$x = \phi(p) f(h_r) \{H(t-h_r) - H(t-h_{r+1})\}, \quad \ldots\ldots\ldots(18)$$

and by superposing contributions from different intervals of time and proceeding to the limit

$$x = -\int_{h=-\infty}^{\infty} \phi(p) S(h)\, dH(t-h), \quad \ldots\ldots\ldots\ldots\ldots(19)$$

which is in general a Stieltjes integral. In this way we obtain a solution, with $H(t)$ regarded as the fundamental function, which replaces decomposition into trigonometrical or exponential functions as in the ordinary treatment.

* Hobson, *Theory of Functions of a Real Variable*, 1 (1921), 507.

CHAPTER II

COMPLEX THEORY

2.1. All the interpretations found so far for the results of operations on unity or on $H(t)$ are special cases of two closely related general rules, as follows. If ϕ is an analytic function,

$$\phi(p) \,.\, 1 = \frac{1}{2\pi\iota}\int_C \frac{e^{\lambda t}}{\lambda}\,\phi(\lambda)\,d\lambda, \quad\text{.................(1)}$$

$$\phi(p)\,H(t) = \frac{1}{2\pi\iota}\int_L \frac{e^{\lambda t}}{\lambda}\,\phi(\lambda)\,d\lambda. \quad\text{...............(2)}$$

In the former definition the integration extends around a large circle in the complex λ plane. In the latter the integration is along a curve from $c - \iota\infty$ to $c + \iota\infty$, where c is positive and finite, and the path is such that all singularities of the integrand are on the left side of the path (that is, the side including $-\infty$). These rules are both due to Bromwich*. We have to show that they agree with the interpretations already given.

Considering first (1) we have, when n is a positive or zero integer,

$$p^{-n} \,.\, 1 = \frac{1}{2\pi\iota}\int_C \frac{e^{\lambda t}}{\lambda^{n+1}}\,d\lambda, \quad\text{....................(3)}$$

and the only pole of the integrand is at the origin, where the residue is $t^n/n!$. Hence when n is a positive integer or zero

$$p^{-n} \,.\, 1 = \frac{t^n}{n!}, \quad\text{..............................(4)}$$

agreeing with the rule of the last chapter.

If $\phi(p)$ is expressible as a power series in p^{-1}, such that on replacing p^{-1} by a number we get a series with a finite radius of convergence, we can write

$$\phi(p) = a_0 + a_1 p^{-1} + \ldots + a_n p^{-n} + \ldots, \quad\text{...........(5)}$$

and by the rule of the last chapter

$$\phi(p) \,.\, 1 = a_0 + a_1 t + \ldots + a_n \frac{t^n}{n!} + \ldots. \quad\text{...........(6)}$$

But by (1) the interpretation is

$$\phi(p) \,.\, 1 = \frac{1}{2\pi\iota}\int_C \frac{e^{\lambda t}}{\lambda}\left(a_0 + \frac{a_1}{\lambda} + \ldots + \frac{a_n}{\lambda^n} + \ldots\right)d\lambda, \quad\text{.........(7)}$$

* 'Normal Coordinates in Dynamical Systems,' *Proc. Lond. Math. Soc.*, 15 (1916), 401–448.

which, we see from (3) and (4), agrees with (6) provided term by term integration is justifiable. To justify it, we notice that the series in $1/\lambda$ converges to a finite sum whenever $|1/\lambda|$ is less than a certain constant r; hence if we write

$$\phi(\lambda) = a_0 + \frac{a_1}{\lambda} + \dots + \frac{a_{n-1}}{\lambda^{n-1}} + R_n(\lambda) \quad \dots\dots\dots\dots(8)$$

and $|\lambda| > 1/r$, we can choose n large enough to make

$$|R_n(\lambda)| < \epsilon \quad \dots\dots\dots\dots(9)$$

everywhere on C, however small ϵ may be. Hence

$$\phi(p).1 = a_0 + a_1 t + \dots + a_{n-1}\frac{t^{n-1}}{(n-1)!} + \frac{1}{2\pi\iota}\int_C \frac{e^{\lambda t}}{\lambda} R_n(\lambda)\, d\lambda. \quad (10)$$

If then C is a circle of radius $1/r$ or more, the last term is less in absolute value than $e^{t/r}\epsilon$. Hence if r is chosen to begin with, we can take ϵ small enough to make $e^{t/r}\epsilon$ less than an arbitrary small quantity η, and then n large enough to make $|R_n(\lambda)|$ less than this ϵ. Thus $\phi(p).1$ differs from the sum of the first n terms of the series by less than an arbitrarily small quantity η, and therefore term by term integration is legitimate.

2.11. Some of our interpretations in finite terms can easily be proved directly. Thus

$$\frac{p}{(p-\alpha)^n}.1 = \frac{1}{2\pi\iota}\int_C \frac{e^{\lambda t}}{(\lambda-\alpha)^n}\, d\lambda = \frac{1}{2\pi\iota} e^{\alpha t}\int_C \frac{e^{(\lambda-\alpha)t}}{(\lambda-\alpha)^n} d\lambda,$$

which has a pole of residue $t^{n-1}/(n-1)!$ at $\lambda = \alpha$. Hence

$$\frac{p}{(p-\alpha)^n}.1 = \frac{t^{n-1}}{(n-1)!} e^{\alpha t} \quad \dots\dots\dots\dots(1)$$

as in 1.5 (5).

Also we can verify the partial-fraction rule. Thus

$$\frac{f(p)}{F(p)}.1 = \frac{1}{2\pi\iota}\int \frac{e^{\lambda t}}{\lambda} \frac{f(\lambda)}{A(\lambda-\alpha_1)(\lambda-\alpha_2)\dots(\lambda-\alpha_n)} d\lambda$$

$$= \frac{f(0)}{F(0)} + \Sigma \frac{f(\alpha)}{\alpha F'(\alpha)} e^{\alpha t} \quad \dots\dots\dots\dots(2)$$

on evaluating the residues at the poles $0, \alpha_1, \alpha_2, \dots \alpha_n$.

2.12. We can also prove directly that 1.4 (3), when interpreted by the rule (1), is the correct solution of equations 1.3 (1). If we denote by $e_{rs}(\lambda)$, $\Delta(\lambda)$, and $E_{rs}(\lambda)$ the results of replacing p by λ in e_{rs}, Δ, and E_{rs}, the part of 1.4 (3) not involving the S_r is equivalent to

$$x_m = \frac{1}{2\pi\iota}\int_C \frac{E_{rm}(\lambda)}{\Delta(\lambda)} v_r e^{\lambda t}\, d\lambda. \quad \dots\dots\dots\dots(1)$$

Substituting in the differential equations and differentiating with regard to t under the integral sign, we get for the left side of the kth equation

$$e_{ks}x_s = \frac{1}{2\pi\iota}\int_C \frac{E_{rs}(\lambda)}{\Delta(\lambda)} e_{ks}(\lambda)\, v_r\, e^{\lambda t}\, d\lambda. \quad \text{.............. (2)}$$

But

$$\left.\begin{aligned} E_{rs}(\lambda)\, e_{ks}(\lambda) &= 0 \text{ if } r \neq k \\ &= \Delta(\lambda) \text{ if } r = k \end{aligned}\right\} \quad \text{.............. (3)}$$

and therefore

$$e_{ks}\, x_s = \frac{1}{2\pi\iota}\int_C v_k e^{\lambda t}\, d\lambda = 0. \quad \text{.................... (4)}$$

Thus the differential equations are satisfied.

Now considering the initial conditions, we put $t=0$, and find

$$x_m = \frac{1}{2\pi\iota}\int_C \frac{E_{rm}(\lambda)}{\Delta(\lambda)} v_r\, d\lambda. \quad \text{.................... (5)}$$

But

$$v_r = a_{rs}\, u_s = \frac{1}{\lambda}\{e_{rs}(\lambda) - b_{rs}\}\, u_s \quad \text{.................. (6)}$$

and

$$x_m = \frac{1}{2\pi\iota}\int_C \frac{E_{rm}(\lambda)}{\lambda\Delta(\lambda)}\{e_{rs}(\lambda) - b_{rs}\}\, u_s\, d\lambda$$

$$= \frac{1}{2\pi\iota}\int_C \left\{\frac{1}{\lambda} u_m - \frac{E_{rm}(\lambda)}{\lambda\Delta(\lambda)} b_{rs} u_s\right\} d\lambda. \quad \text{............ (7)}$$

Now $\Delta(\lambda)$ is a polynomial of the nth degree in λ, and $E_{rm}(\lambda)$ one of the $(n-1)$th degree. When $|\lambda|$ is great enough the second term in the integrand is therefore of order λ^{-2}, and gives zero on integration. Hence

$$x_m = u_m \quad \text{.......................... (8)}$$

and the initial conditions are satisfied.

Next, suppose that instead of the S's being zero they are exponential terms of the form $Pe^{\mu t}$. Since the solutions are additive it is enough to suppose that the initial values of the y's are all zero, and to consider the effect of an exponential term in the first equation alone. Then the equations are

$$\left.\begin{aligned} &e_{11}y_1 + e_{12}y_2 + \dots + e_{1n}y_n = Pe^{\mu t} = \frac{Pp}{p-\mu} \\ &e_{rs}y_s = 0 \quad (r \neq 1) \end{aligned}\right\}. \quad \text{......... (9)}$$

The operational solution is

$$y_s = \frac{E_{1s}}{\Delta}\frac{Pp}{p-\mu}. \quad \text{...................... (10)}$$

This is to be interpreted as

$$y_s = \frac{1}{2\pi\iota}\int_C \frac{E_{1s}(\lambda)}{\Delta(\lambda)}\frac{P}{\lambda-\mu} e^{\lambda t}\, d\lambda. \quad \text{.............. (11)}$$

Substituting in the differential equations we find that the left sides of all vanish except the first, in consequence of the integrand containing as a factor a determinant with two rows identical; the first gives

$$\frac{P}{2\pi\iota}\int_C \frac{e^{\lambda t}}{\lambda-\mu}\,d\lambda = Pe^{\mu t}. \quad\text{..................}(12)$$

The differential equations are therefore satisfied.

When $t=0$ and $|\lambda|$ is large, the integrands in (11) are all $O(\lambda^{-2})$ and the integrals are therefore zero. Thus all the x's vanish with t.

Since all functions that occur in physics can be expressed by Fourier's theorems as linear combinations of exponentials, the proof that the solution can be carried out by operational methods is complete. We shall see later, however, that Fourier's theorems are not so convenient to use as the formula 1.9 (19) based on the function $H(t)$.

2.2. Now let us consider the integral 2.1 (2), taken along the path L. If we suppose the contour completed by a large semicircle from $c+\iota\infty$ to $c-\iota\infty$ by way of $-\infty$, all the singularities of the integrand are within the contour, and therefore the integral around it is the same as the integral (1) around a large circle. Now if t is positive, and $\phi(\lambda)/\lambda$ tends to zero uniformly with regard to arg λ as λ tends to ∞, the integral around a large semicircle tends to zero as the radius becomes indefinitely large, by Jordan's lemma*. Hence the integral along L is equivalent to the integral around a large circle. Thus if t is positive and

$$\phi(\lambda)/\lambda = O(\lambda^{-n})$$

when λ is great and n is positive, $\phi(p)\,H(t)$ is the same as $\phi(p)\,1$. But if t is negative, the integral around the large semicircle on the negative side of the imaginary axis is no longer an instance of Jordan's lemma, and this result no longer holds. The integral around a large semicircle on the *positive* side of the imaginary axis is, however, reducible to the integral along L, since by construction there is no singularity between these two paths. If then $\phi(\lambda)/\lambda = O(\lambda^{-n})$ when λ is great, the limit of the integral around this large semicircle is zero by Jordan's lemma, and therefore $\phi(p)\,H(t)$ is zero.

Thus if $\phi(p)$ is expansible in descending powers of p, beginning with a constant or a negative power of p, we shall have

$$\left.\begin{array}{ll}\phi(p)\,H(t)=\phi(p)\,1 & \text{when } t>0\\ \phi(p)\,H(t)=0 & \text{when } t<0\end{array}\right\}, \quad\text{...........}(1)$$

and the results agree with those of Chapter I.

* Whittaker and Watson, *Modern Analysis*, 1915, 115.

2.3. The form 2.1 (1) suggests an interpretation of p^n, where n is a positive integer. For it gives

$$p^n \, . \, 1 = \frac{1}{2\pi\iota}\int_C \lambda^{n-1} e^{\lambda t}\, d\lambda$$
$$= 0, \quad \text{......(1)}$$

since the integrand has no singularity in the finite part of the plane. This result is the same as is obtained by interpreting p as d/dt.

If $\phi(p)$ is expansible in negative powers of p as in 2.1 (5), we have

$$\frac{d}{dt}\{\phi(p) \, . \, 1\} = \frac{d}{dt}\frac{1}{2\pi\iota}\int_C \frac{e^{\lambda t}}{\lambda}\phi(\lambda)\, d\lambda$$
$$= \frac{1}{2\pi\iota}\int_C e^{\lambda t}\phi(\lambda)\, d\lambda, \quad \text{......(2)}$$

since differentiation of a contour integral may be carried out under the integral sign.

But (2) is the interpretation, according to 2.1 (1), of $p\,\phi(p) \, . \, 1$. Hence if we have an operator involving both definite integrations and differentiations, and we replace definite integration by p^{-1} and differentiation by p, and interpret according to 2.1 (1), we get the result of carrying out the differentiations *after* the integrations. The complex integral interpretation is therefore consistent with 1.8.

2.31. Again, if the operator $\phi(p)$ acting on unity gives $f(t)$, and we seek for an interpretation of $e^{hp} f(t)$, we have

$$e^{hp} f(t) = e^{hp} \, . \, \phi(p) \, . \, 1 = \frac{1}{2\pi\iota}\int_C \frac{e^{\lambda(t+h)}}{\lambda}\left(a_0 + \frac{a_1}{\lambda} + \ldots + \frac{a_n}{\lambda^2} + \ldots\right) d\lambda \quad (1)$$

and the residues given by the various terms are the same as in the interpretation of $\phi(p) \, . \, 1$ except that t is replaced by $t+h$. Hence

$$e^{hp} f(t) = f(t+h). \quad \text{......(2)}$$

If the operator $\phi(p)$ acting on $H(t)$ gives $f(t)$, we may proceed similarly, using the line L instead of C; again the form (2) holds. This gives the justification for 1.9 (6); for any bounded function can be expressed in terms of $H(t)$ by 1.9 (15), whether it is expansible in a power series or not. We had

$$f(t) = -\int_{h=-\infty}^{\infty} f(h)\, d\left[e^{-ph} H(t)\right], \quad \text{......(3)}$$

and the right side, interpreted by 2.1 (2), gives

$$f(t) = -\frac{1}{2\pi\iota}\int_{h=-\infty}^{\infty} f(h)\, d\left[\int_L \frac{e^{\lambda(t-h)}}{\lambda}\, d\lambda\right]$$
$$= \frac{1}{2\pi\iota}\int_{-\infty}^{\infty}\int_L f(h)\, e^{\lambda(t-h)}\, dh\, d\lambda. \quad \text{......(4)}$$

On L we may put

$$\lambda = c + \iota\kappa, \quad \text{..........................(5)}$$

where c is real and positive. Then

$$f(t) = \frac{1}{2\pi}\int_{-\infty}^{\infty}\int_{-\infty}^{\infty} f(h)\, e^{c(t-h)} e^{\iota\kappa(t-h)}\, dh\, d\kappa$$

$$= \frac{1}{\pi}\int_{-\infty}^{\infty}\int_{0}^{\infty} f(h)\, e^{c(t-h)} \cos\kappa(t-h)\, dh\, d\kappa. \quad \text{............(6)}$$

We may rewrite this as

$$f(t)\, e^{-ct} = \frac{1}{\pi}\int_{-\infty}^{\infty}\int_{0}^{\infty} f(h)\, e^{-ch} \cos\kappa(t-h)\, dh\, d\kappa, \quad \text{.........(7)}$$

so that (6) is equivalent to Fourier's integral theorem applied to the function $f(t)\, e^{-ct}$. It is therefore more general than this theorem applied to $f(t)$ directly; for with c equal to zero the integrals may diverge, but the theorem may be saved by giving c a finite positive value. But just as the interpretation of $\phi(p) H(t)$ is usually independent of the value of c, so here the value of the integral is independent of c so long as it exceeds a certain value, which in many practical cases is zero.

In practice the form 2.1 (2) or a modification of it is generally used in preference to 2.1 (1). In problems involving a finite number of ordinary differential equations of the first order the forms are equivalent for all positive values of the independent variable; and since the independent variable is usually the time, and we require to know how a system will behave if it is in a known state at time 0 and is afterwards acted upon by known disturbances, it is as a rule only positive values of the time that concern us. Then an integral along L is equivalent to one around C. Indeed if instead of L we take a curved path beginning in the third quadrant, passing the origin on the positive side, and receding to infinity anywhere in the second quadrant, provided we still keep all poles on the left of the path, we shall obtain the same value for positive values of t; this integral in general will diverge for negative values of t.

But when we come to deal with continuous systems it usually happens that when the operational solution $\phi(p)$ is interpreted as an integral, the integrand has an infinite number of poles, and that no circle however large can include all of them. Hence the contour integral 2.1 (1) cannot be formed. But the line integral along L usually still exists. Again, it may happen that $\phi(\lambda)$ has a branch-point at the origin or on the negative side of the imaginary axis. Here again the contour integral does not exist, but the line integral does.

Consequently in most of the writings of Heaviside and Bromwich, when a function of an operator $\phi(p)$ occurs without the operand being specified explicitly, it is to be understood that the operand is $H(t)$, and that the interpretation 2.1 (2) or a suitable modification of it is to be adopted. This rule will be followed in this work when we come to deal with continuous systems; and if it is also supposed to be adopted in the problems of the next chapter no harm will be done.

Considerable latitude is seen to be permissible in choosing the path L. Since by construction the integrand is regular at all points to the right of L, we can replace L by any path on its positive side provided it ends at $c \pm \iota\infty$. Again, the systems we discuss are usually stable systems: that is, the poles of $\phi(\lambda)$ are all on the imaginary axis or to the left of it. Then L can be taken as near as we like to the imaginary axis. L must not cross the imaginary axis if there are poles on the latter with

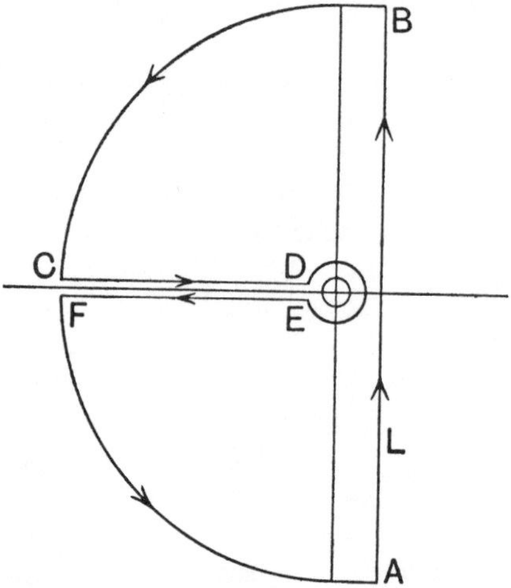

Fig. 1.

indefinitely great values of the argument. Bromwich's usual device is to take L parallel to the imaginary axis and any constant distance c from it; by our restriction that all singularities must be to the left of L, however, we avoid a possible ambiguity for unstable systems. By allowing L to begin and end *within* the third and second quadrants we ensure convergence in some cases when it would otherwise fail, but this is never, so far as I know, necessary in the actual solution of a physical problem, though it is often useful in the course of evaluation, as in 2.4 (22).

2.4. The principal operators involving branch-points are fractional powers of p. We require then an interpretation of $p^m H(t)$, where m is a positive or negative fraction*. By our rule

$$p^m H(t) = \frac{1}{2\pi\iota}\int_L \lambda^{m-1} e^{\lambda t}\, d\lambda \quad \text{.....................(1)}$$

when t is positive. The integral converges if $m < 1$; but if L is replaced by a path L' such that the ends are in the second and third quadrants and make finite angles with the imaginary axis, the integral will converge for any value of m. There is a branch-point at $\lambda = 0$.

A contour containing L as part of itself, and such that the integral is regular within it, is as shown. Evidently the large quadrants make no contribution, subject to the proviso that if $m > 1$ we replace L by L'. The integral along L or L' is therefore in the limit equal and opposite to one along $CDEF$. If further m is positive the contribution from DE tends to zero with the radius of DE. Now on CD and EF

$$\lambda = \mu e^{\iota\pi} \text{ and } \mu e^{-\iota\pi} \quad \text{.......................(2)}$$

respectively, where μ is real and positive. Hence on CD

$$\lambda^{m-1} e^{\lambda t}\, d\lambda = -\mu^{m-1} e^{-\mu t} e^{(m-1)\iota\pi}\, d\mu = \mu^{m-1} e^{-\mu t} e^{m\iota\pi}\, d\mu, \quad \text{......(3)}$$

and on EF

$$\lambda^{m-1} e^{\lambda t}\, d\lambda = -\mu^{m-1} e^{-\mu t} e^{-(m-1)\iota\pi}\, d\mu = \mu^{m-1} e^{-\mu t} e^{-m\iota\pi}\, d\mu. \quad \text{......(4)}$$

Thus

$$2\pi\iota\, p^m H(t) = -\int_\infty^0 \mu^{m-1} e^{-\mu t} e^{m\iota\pi}\, d\mu - \int_0^\infty \mu^{m-1} e^{-\mu t} e^{-m\iota\pi}\, d\mu$$

$$= 2\iota \sin m\pi \int_0^\infty \mu^{m-1} e^{-\mu t}\, d\mu. \quad \text{....................(5)}$$

But if we introduce Gauss's Π-function, defined for positive values of m by the equation

$$\Pi(m) = \Gamma(m+1) = \int_0^\infty e^{-u} u^m\, du, \quad \text{..............(6)}$$

and for negative values of m by the inductive equation

$$\Pi(m) = m\,\Pi(m-1), \quad \text{.......................(7)}$$

we have
$$\int_0^\infty \mu^{m-1} e^{-\mu t}\, d\mu = t^{-m}\,\Pi(m-1) = t^{-m}\frac{\Pi(m)}{m}. \quad \text{........(8)}$$

Hence
$$p^m H(t) = \frac{\Pi(m)}{m\pi}\sin m\pi \,.\, t^{-m}. \quad \text{.................(9)}$$

* Cf. Bromwich, *Proc. Camb. Phil. Soc.*, 20 (1921), 411–427.

But by a known theorem

$$\Pi(m)\,\Pi(-m) = m\pi \operatorname{cosec} m\pi, \quad \text{.............(10)}$$

and therefore

$$p^m H(t) = \frac{t^{-m}}{\Pi(-m)}. \quad \text{.......................(11)}$$

This has been proved for positive values of m. But if we define $p^{m+1} H(t)$ for any value of m by 2.1 (2) with L' for L we have

$$\begin{aligned} p^{m+1} H(t) &= \frac{1}{2\pi\iota}\int_{L'} \lambda^m e^{\lambda t}\, d\lambda \\ &= \frac{1}{2\pi\iota}\int_{L'} \frac{1}{t}\lambda^m d\left(e^{\lambda t}\right) \\ &= \frac{1}{2\pi\iota}\left[\frac{\lambda^m}{t} e^{\lambda t}\right] - \frac{1}{2\pi\iota t}\int_{L'} m\lambda^{m-1} e^{\lambda t}\, d\lambda. \quad \text{......(12)} \end{aligned}$$

The integrated part vanishes at both limits. The integral is $-\frac{m}{t} p^m H(t)$. When m is positive we can apply (11) and get

$$p^{m+1} H(t) = -\frac{m}{t}\cdot\frac{t^{-m}}{\Pi(-m)} = \frac{t^{-m-1}}{\Pi(-m-1)}, \quad \text{.........(13)}$$

which could also be obtained by putting $m+1$ for m in (11). But we can also put

$$p^m H(t) = -\frac{t}{m} p^{m+1} H(t) = -\frac{t}{m}\frac{t^{-m-1}}{\Pi(-m-1)} = \frac{t^{-m}}{\Pi(-m)}, \quad (14)$$

which extends (11) to values of m that make $m+1$ positive. Hence (11) is true for $m > -1$. By repetition we can show that it holds for all values of m. If we change m into $-n$ we have for all values of n,

$$p^{-n} H(t) = \frac{t^n}{\Pi(n)}. \quad \text{....................(15)}$$

Since when n is a positive integer $\Pi(n) = n!$ and when n is a negative integer $\Pi(n)$ is infinite, the interpretations already adopted for integral powers of p are special cases of (15).

If we differentiate (15) with regard to n, we have formally

$$-p^{-n}\log p = \frac{t^n \log t}{\Pi(n)} - \frac{t^n\,\Pi'(n)}{\{\Pi(n)\}^2},$$

and if then n tends to 0,

$$-\log p = \log t - \Pi'(0)/\Pi(0).$$

But $-\Pi'(0)/\Pi(0)$ is Euler's constant γ, and

$$\log p = -\gamma - \log t.$$

We notice also that

$$\frac{d}{dt} p^m H(t) = \frac{d}{dt} \frac{t^{-m}}{\Pi(-m)} = -\frac{m}{\Pi(-m)} t^{-m-1} = \frac{t^{-m-1}}{\Pi(-m-1)} = p^{m+1} H(t), \quad \text{.........(16)}$$

$$\int_0^t p^{m+1} H(t)\, dt = \left[\frac{t^{-m}}{\Pi(-m)}\right]_0^t = \frac{t^{-m}}{\Pi(-m)} = p^m H(t), \quad \text{...(17)}$$

provided m is negative. Hence the differentiation is equivalent to multiplying by p and reinterpreting; and integration is equivalent to dividing by p and reinterpreting, provided the result of integration vanishes when $t = 0$.

In particular, since

$$\Pi(-\tfrac{1}{2}) = \Gamma(\tfrac{1}{2}) = \surd\pi, \quad \text{....................(18)}$$

we have

$$p^{\frac{1}{2}} H(t) = \frac{1}{\surd(\pi t)};\quad p^{\frac{3}{2}} = -\frac{1}{2\surd\pi} t^{-\frac{3}{2}};\quad p^{\frac{5}{2}} = \tfrac{1}{2} \cdot \tfrac{3}{2} \cdot \frac{1}{\surd\pi} t^{-\frac{5}{2}}; \quad \text{...(19)}$$

and so on. Also

$$p^{-\frac{1}{2}} = 2\sqrt{\frac{t}{\pi}};\quad p^{-\frac{3}{2}} = 2 \cdot \tfrac{2}{3} \frac{t^{\frac{3}{2}}}{\surd\pi};\quad p^{-\frac{5}{2}} = 2 \cdot \tfrac{2}{3} \cdot \tfrac{2}{5} \frac{t^{\frac{5}{2}}}{\surd\pi}. \quad \text{......(20)}$$

A related function that occurs in problems of heat conduction is e^{-aq}, where a is a constant, and q denotes $p^{\frac{1}{2}}$. By 2.1 (2)

$$e^{-aq} H(t) = \frac{1}{2\pi\iota} \int_L \frac{e^{\lambda t - a\lambda^{\frac{1}{2}}}}{\lambda} d\lambda. \quad \text{..................(21)}$$

On L the argument of $\lambda^{\frac{1}{2}}$ is between $\pm\frac{1}{4}\pi$. Hence if a is positive the integral is convergent.

Immediate expansion of $e^{-a\lambda^{\frac{1}{2}}}$ in a power series and integration term by term would not be legitimate, because all the resulting integrals after the first two would diverge when taken along the path L. But if instead we use a path L', (21) is unaffected, and on L' we can proceed in this way. Thus

$$e^{-qa} H(t) = \frac{1}{2\pi\iota} \int_{L'} \frac{e^{\lambda t}}{\lambda} \left[1 - a\lambda^{\frac{1}{2}} + \frac{a^2\lambda}{2!} - \frac{a^3\lambda^{\frac{3}{2}}}{3!} + \dots\right] d\lambda. \quad \text{...(22)}$$

All the positive integral powers of λ give zero on integration. The other terms are equivalent to

$$1 - ap^{\frac{1}{2}} - \frac{a^3 p^{\frac{3}{2}}}{3!} - \frac{a^5 p^{\frac{5}{2}}}{5!} - \dots$$

$$= 1 - \frac{2}{\surd\pi}\left\{\frac{a}{2\surd t} - \frac{1}{3}\left(\frac{a}{2\surd t}\right)^3 + \frac{1}{2!\,5}\left(\frac{a}{2\surd t}\right)^5 - \dots\right\} = 1 - \operatorname{erf}\frac{a}{2\surd t}, \quad \text{......(23)}$$

where, by definition,

$$\operatorname{erf} w = \frac{2}{\sqrt{\pi}} \int_0^w e^{-t^2} dt. \quad \text{..................(24)}$$

By differentiation with regard to a we find

$$q e^{-qa} H(t) = \frac{1}{\sqrt{(\pi t)}} e^{-a^2/4t}. \quad \text{..................(25)}$$

We shall sometimes need an asymptotic approximation to erf w when w is great. We have

$$1 - \operatorname{erf} w = \frac{2}{\sqrt{\pi}} \int_w^\infty e^{-t^2} dt = \frac{1}{\sqrt{\pi}} \int_{w^2}^\infty e^{-u} u^{-\frac{1}{2}} du$$

$$= \frac{1}{\sqrt{\pi}} e^{-w^2} w^{-1} \left[1 - \frac{1}{2} w^{-2} + \frac{1.3}{2.2} w^{-4} - \frac{1.3.5}{2.2.2} w^{-6} + \dots \right]$$

$$+ \frac{(-1)^n}{\sqrt{\pi}} \frac{1.3.5 \dots (2n-1)}{2.2.2 \dots \quad 2} \int_{w^2}^\infty e^{-u} u^{-\frac{1}{2}(2n+1)} du, \quad (26)$$

on successive integrations by parts. But the last integral

$$= 2 \int_w^\infty e^{-t^2} t^{-2n} dt < 2 e^{-w^2} \int_w^\infty t^{-2n} dt$$

$$< \frac{2 e^{-w^2}}{2n-1} w^{-(2n-1)}, \quad \text{..............(27)}$$

so that its contribution to the function is less than the previous term. We have therefore the asymptotic approximation

$$e^{w^2} (1 - \operatorname{erf} w) \sim \frac{1}{\sqrt{\pi}} \left[w^{-1} - \frac{1}{2} w^{-3} + \frac{1.3}{2.2} w^{-5} - \frac{1.3.5}{2.2.2} w^{-7} + \dots \right]. \quad (28)$$

2.5. *Carson's method.* In this method p is not regarded as an operator but as a quantity. If we return to 1.9 (15)

$$f(t) = - \int_{h=-\infty}^{\infty} f(h)\, d\,[e^{-ph} H(t)] \quad \text{..............(1)}$$

we can write formally

$$g(p) = \int_{-\infty}^{\infty} p f(h)\, e^{-ph} dh \quad \text{....................(2)}$$

and then

$$g(p) H(t) = f(t). \quad \text{........................(3)}$$

But (2) is actually perfectly intelligible if p is a quantity instead of an operator. Then (2), if $g(p)$ is known, is an integral equation to determine $f(h)$. Some restriction on $f(h)$ is implied by the convergence of the integral; in practice $f(h)$ vanishes when h is negative, so that h is only allowed to proceed from 0 to ∞, and p is taken to have a positive real part. Then (2) becomes

$$g(p)=\int_0^\infty pf(h)\,e^{-ph}\,dh, \quad\text{.....................(4)}$$

an equation to determine $f(h)$ for positive values of h. This is Carson's integral equation. Here, however, (2) will be used.

Now the integral

$$\frac{1}{2\pi\iota}\int_L \frac{g(p)}{p}e^{pt}\,dp=\frac{1}{2\pi\iota}\int_{-\infty}^{\infty}\int_L f(h)\,e^{p(t-h)}\,dh\,dp$$
$$=f(t), \quad\text{.................................(5)}$$

for the double integral in (5) is simply that in 2.31 (4) with p written for λ. Thus the solution of (2) is

$$f(t)=\frac{1}{2\pi\iota}\int_L \frac{g(p)}{p}e^{pt}\,dp. \quad\text{.....................(6)}$$

This proves that Bromwich's integral is the solution of Carson's equation, as has been pointed out by Lévy and March.

CHAPTER III

PHYSICAL APPLICATIONS: ONE INDEPENDENT VARIABLE

3.1. An electric circuit contains a cell, a condenser, and a coil with self-induction and resistance. Initially the circuit is open. It is suddenly completed; find how the charge on the plates varies with the time.

Let y be the charge on the plates, t the time, K the capacity of the condenser, L the self-induction, and R the resistance of the circuit; and let E be the electromotive force of the cell. Write p for d/dt.

The current in the circuit is $\dot{y}$, and the charging of the plates of the condenser produces a potential difference y/K tending to oppose the original E.M.F. Then y satisfies the differential equation

$$E-\frac{y}{K}=L\ddot{y}+R\dot{y}. \quad\text{.......................(1)}$$

Initially y and $\dot{y}$, the current, are zero. Hence the subsidiary equation is simply

$$\left(Lp^2+Rp+\frac{1}{K}\right)y=E, \quad\text{.....................(2)}$$

and the solution is

$$y = \frac{E}{Lp^2 + Rp + \dfrac{1}{K}}. \quad \text{.......................(3)}$$

If now the denominator is expressed in the form $L(p+\alpha)(p+\beta)$, the interpretation is, by 1.5 (9),

$$y = \frac{E}{L}\left[KL + \frac{1}{\alpha-\beta}\left(\frac{1}{\alpha}e^{-\alpha t} - \frac{1}{\beta}e^{-\beta t}\right)\right]. \quad \text{............(4)}$$

Since $\alpha+\beta$ and $\alpha\beta$ are both positive, α and β must be both real and positive, or else conjugate imaginaries with positive real parts. In either case y tends to KE as a limit, as we should expect.

We notice incidentally that if the circuit contained no capacity or self-induction the differential equation would be simply

$$R\dot{y} = E. \quad \text{..............................(5)}$$

Hence if the current has been found for simple resistances, self-induction and capacity can be allowed for by writing $Lp + R + \dfrac{1}{Kp}$ for R. For this reason this expression is sometimes called a 'resistance operator,' and the method generally the 'method of resistance operators.'

3.2. *The Wheatstone Bridge method of determining Self-Induction.* In this method the unknown inductance is placed in the first arm of a Wheatstone bridge; the fourth arm is shunted, a known capacity being placed in the shunt*.

First consider the ordinary Wheatstone bridge, the resistances of the arms being R_1, R_2, R_3, R_4; let x be the current in R_1, y that in R_2, g that through the galvanometer, and b the resistance of the battery and leads.

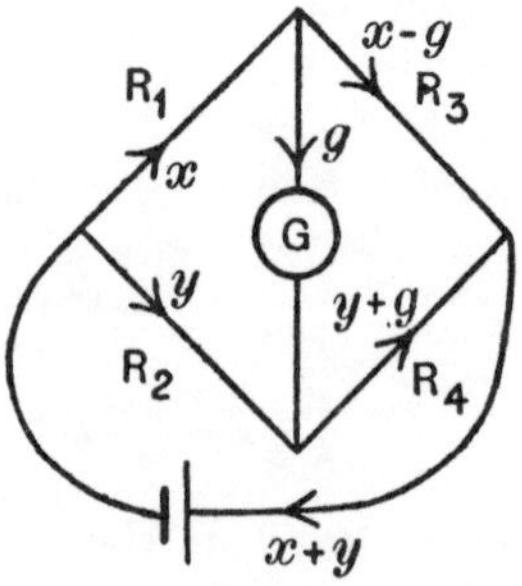

Fig. 2.

* Bromwich, *Phil. Mag.*, 37 (1919), 407–419. Further references are given.

Then
$$R_1 x - R_2 y + Gg = 0, \quad \ldots\ldots\ldots\ldots\ldots(1)$$
$$R_3 x - R_4 y - (R_3 + R_4 + G)\, g = 0, \quad \ldots\ldots\ldots\ldots\ldots(2)$$
$$b\,(x+y) + R_2 y + R_4\,(y+g) = E, \quad \ldots\ldots\ldots\ldots\ldots(3)$$

and on solving we find

$$\frac{g}{R_2 R_3 - R_1 R_4} = \frac{x+y}{G\,(R_1+R_2+R_3+R_4) + (R_1+R_2)\,(R_3+R_4)}. \quad (4)$$

If b is large compared with R_2 and R_4, we have nearly

$$x + y = E/b, \quad \ldots\ldots\ldots\ldots\ldots\ldots\ldots\ldots\ldots(5)$$

and
$$g = \frac{(E/b)\,(R_2 R_3 - R_1 R_4)}{G\,(R_1+R_2+R_3+R_4) + (R_1+R_2)\,(R_3+R_4)}. \quad \ldots\ldots(6)$$

According to the result of 3.1, we can allow for the self-induction in the first arm by replacing R_1 by $Lp + R_1$. Let the arrangement in the

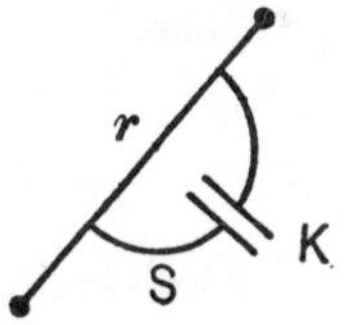

Fig. 3.

fourth arm be as shown (Fig. 3). The resistance of the main wire is R_4, that of the shunted portion of it r. Suppose the shunt to have a resistance S. Then the effective resistance of the whole arm would be

$$R_4 - r + \frac{rS}{r+S} = R_4 - \frac{r^2}{r+S}. \quad \ldots\ldots\ldots\ldots\ldots\ldots(7)$$

If the shunt contains a capacity K, we must replace S by $S + 1/Kp$. Hence in the formula for g we must replace R_1 by $Lp + R_1$ and R_4 by

$$R_4 - \frac{r^2 Kp}{(r+S)\,Kp + 1}.$$

The result expresses the current through the galvanometer when the battery circuit is suddenly closed.

It can be shown that in actual conditions g cannot vanish for all values of the time. A sufficient condition for this would be that the operator $R_2 R_3 - R_1 R_4$ should be identically zero; then g would be identically zero whatever the remaining factor might represent. But with our modifications this factor becomes

$$R_2 R_3 - (Lp + R_1)\left(R_4 - \frac{r^2 Kp}{(r+S)\,Kp + 1}\right). \quad \ldots\ldots\ldots\ldots(8)$$

Multiplying up and equating coefficients of powers of p to zero, we find

$$R_4(r+S)=r^2, \quad \text{.........................(9)}$$

$$-LR_4+(R_2R_3-R_1R_4)(r+S)K+R_1r^2K=0, \quad \text{......(10)}$$

$$R_2R_3-R_1R_4=0. \quad \text{.......................(11)}$$

From the construction of the apparatus $r \leqslant R_4$, $r \leqslant r+S$. Thus (9) can hold only if $r=R_4$ and $S=0$. The shunt wire must be attached to the ends of R_4 and must have zero resistance. Substituting in (10) we find

$$L=R_1R_4K, \quad \text{.........................(12)}$$

together with the usual condition (11) for permanent balance of the bridge.

Actually these conditions for complete balance cannot be completely satisfied; but for the determination of L it is not necessary that they should. Suppose the galvanometer is a ballistic one, and that it is so adjusted that there are no permanent current and no throw on closing the circuit. Thus

$$\lim_{t\to\infty} g=0; \quad \int_0^\infty g\,dt=0. \quad \text{....................(13)}$$

If g is expressed in the form $f(p)/F(p)$, we have

$$g=\frac{f(0)}{F(0)}+\Sigma\frac{f(\alpha)}{\alpha F'(\alpha)}e^{\alpha t}, \quad \text{..................(14)}$$

where all the α's, in the conditions of the problem, will have negative real parts. Then the condition that g shall tend to zero gives

$$f(0)=0. \quad \text{............................(15)}$$

Also

$$\int_0^\infty g\,dt=-\Sigma\frac{f(\alpha)}{\alpha^2F'(\alpha)}. \quad \text{..................(16)}$$

Equation (15) shows that the operational form of g contains p as a factor. Also we can write

$$g=\Sigma\frac{f(\alpha)}{\alpha F'(\alpha)}\frac{p}{p-\alpha}, \quad \text{....................(17)}$$

so that (16) is the limit of g/p when p tends to zero. The vanishing of $\operatorname{Lim} g$ and $\int_0^\infty g\,dt$ implies therefore that the operational form of g contains p^2 as a factor. Hence the modified form of $R_2R_3-R_1R_4$ must contain p^2 as a factor. Then (10) and (11) still hold; (9) no longer holds. We now have

$$R_2R_3-R_1R_4=0, \quad \text{.......................(18)}$$

$$LR_4=R_1r^2K, \quad \text{.......................(19)}$$

which gives the required rule for finding L.

3.21. *Discharge of a condenser in one of two mutually influencing circuits.* Suppose that we have two similar circuits, each with self-induction L and capacity K, but negligible resistance, and that the condenser in one carries a charge x_0. The coefficient of mutual induction is M. The first circuit is closed; find the currents.

If x, y denote the charges on the condensers in the two circuits, we have the differential equations

$$\left.\begin{aligned} L\ddot{x} + M\ddot{y} + L\alpha^2 x = 0, \\ M\ddot{x} + L\ddot{y} + L\alpha^2 y = 0, \end{aligned}\right\} \quad \text{.....................(1)}$$

where
$$KL\alpha^2 = 1. \quad \text{..............................(2)}$$

Initially
$$x = x_0, \; y = 0, \; \dot{x} = \dot{y} = 0. \quad \text{.....................(3)}$$

The subsidiary equations are

$$\left.\begin{aligned} L(p^2 + \alpha^2)\, x + Mp^2 y = Lp^2 x_0, \\ Mp^2 x + L(p^2 + \alpha^2)\, y = Mp^2 x_0. \end{aligned}\right\} \quad \text{..............(4)}$$

Then solving by algebra

$$x = \frac{L^2(p^2+\alpha^2) - M^2p^2}{L^2(p^2+\alpha^2)^2 - M^2p^4} p^2 x_0; \quad y = \frac{LM\alpha^2 p^2}{L^2(p^2+\alpha^2)^2 - M^2p^4} x_0. \quad (5)$$

Put $M = L\beta$. Then

$$L^2(p^2+\alpha^2)^2 - M^2p^4 = L^2(p^2+\alpha^2-\beta p^2)(p^2+\alpha^2+\beta p^2); \;\text{...(6)}$$

$$x = \frac{p^2(1-\beta^2)+\alpha^2}{\{(1-\beta)p^2+\alpha^2\}\{(1+\beta)p^2+\alpha^2\}} p^2 x_0$$

$$= \left[\frac{(1-\beta)p^2}{(1-\beta)p^2+\alpha^2} + \frac{(1+\beta)p^2}{(1+\beta)p^2+\alpha^2}\right]\tfrac{1}{2}x_0$$

$$= \left[\cos\frac{\alpha}{\sqrt{1-\beta}}t + \cos\frac{\alpha}{\sqrt{1+\beta}}t\right]\tfrac{1}{2}x_0; \quad \text{...........(7)}$$

$$y = \frac{\beta\alpha^2}{\{(1-\beta)p^2+\alpha^2\}\{(1+\beta)p^2+\alpha^2\}} p^2 x_0$$

$$= -\tfrac{1}{2}\left[\frac{1-\beta}{(1-\beta)p^2+\alpha^2} - \frac{1+\beta}{(1+\beta)p^2+\alpha^2}\right] p^2 x_0$$

$$= -\tfrac{1}{2}\left[\cos\frac{\alpha}{\sqrt{1-\beta}}t - \cos\frac{\alpha}{\sqrt{1+\beta}}t\right] x_0. \quad \text{...........(8)}$$

If we write
$$\frac{\alpha}{\sqrt{1-\beta}} = \gamma + \delta; \quad \frac{\alpha}{\sqrt{1+\beta}} = \gamma - \delta, \quad \text{..............(9)}$$

the solutions take the forms

$$\left.\begin{aligned} x = x_0 \cos\gamma t \cos\delta t, \\ y = x_0 \sin\gamma t \sin\delta t. \end{aligned}\right\} \quad \text{.....................(10)}$$

Thus when β/α is small the disturbance consists of a rapid oscillation with beats, the oscillation being transferred from one circuit to the other in each quarter-period of the beats.

3.3. *The Seismograph.* In principle most seismographs are Euler pendulums—pendulums with supports rigidly attached to the earth, so that when the earth's surface moves it displaces the point of support horizontally and disturbs the pendulum. The seismograph differs from the Euler pendulum as considered in text-books of dynamics in two ways: instead of being free to vibrate in a vertical plane, it is constrained to swing, like a gate, about an axis nearly, but not quite, vertical, so that the period is much lengthened; and fluid viscosity or electromagnetic damping is introduced to give a frictional term proportional to the velocity. The displacement of the mass with regard to the earth then satisfies an equation of the form

$$\ddot{x} + 2\kappa\dot{x} + n^2 x = \lambda\ddot{\xi}, \quad \text{.......................(1)}$$

where ξ is the displacement of the ground, and κ, n, and λ are constants of the instrument*. Suppose first that the ground suddenly acquires a finite velocity, say unity. Then $\dot{\xi}$ jumps from 0 to 1, and therefore $\dot{x}$ from 0 to λ. The initial conditions are therefore

$$x = 0; \quad \dot{x} = \lambda, \quad \text{.........................(2)}$$

and our subsidiary equation is

$$(p^2 + 2\kappa p + n^2)\, x = \lambda p H(t). \quad \text{.................(3)}$$

Put

$$p^2 + 2\kappa p + n^2 = (p + \alpha)(p + \beta). \quad \text{.................(4)}$$

Then

$$x = \frac{\lambda p}{(p + \alpha)(p + \beta)} H(t) \quad \text{....................(5)}$$

$$= 0 \text{ when } t < 0 \text{...............................(6)}$$

and

$$= \frac{\lambda}{\alpha - \beta}(e^{-\beta t} - e^{-\alpha t}) \text{ when } t > 0. \quad \text{...........(7)}$$

The recorded displacement x therefore begins by increasing at a finite rate λ, reaches a maximum $\lambda\left(\frac{\beta^\beta}{\alpha^\alpha}\right)^{\frac{1}{\alpha-\beta}}$ after a time $\frac{1}{\alpha - \beta}\log\frac{\alpha}{\beta}$, and then tends asymptotically to zero.

* Some instruments, such as that of Wiechert, are not on the principle of the Euler pendulum, but nevertheless give an equation of this form.

If α and β are real, and β less than α, we see that the behaviour after a long time depends mainly on $e^{-\beta t}$; now as the experimental ideal is to confine the effects of a disturbance to as short an interval afterwards as possible, we see that we should make β as large as possible. But

$$\beta = \kappa - (\kappa^2 - n^2)^{\frac{1}{2}} = \frac{n^2}{\kappa + (\kappa^2 - n^2)^{\frac{1}{2}}}, \quad \text{.................}(8)$$

and for a given n, β is greatest when $\kappa = n$. This is the condition for what is called aperiodicity; the roots of the period equation are equal, real, and negative. Many seismographs are arranged so as to satisfy this condition. The solution is then

$$x = \frac{\lambda p}{(p+n)^2} H(t) \quad \text{.........................}(9)$$

$$= 0 \text{ when } t < 0 \text{.........................}(10)$$

$$= \lambda t e^{-nt} \text{ when } t > 0. \quad \text{.................}(11)$$

The maximum displacement is now at time $1/n$ after the start, and is equal to λ/en.

If $\kappa < n$, we can put

$$n^2 - \kappa^2 = \gamma^2. \quad \text{...........................}(12)$$

Then the solution is

$$x = \frac{\lambda}{\gamma} e^{-\kappa t} \sin \gamma t, \quad \text{.......................}(13)$$

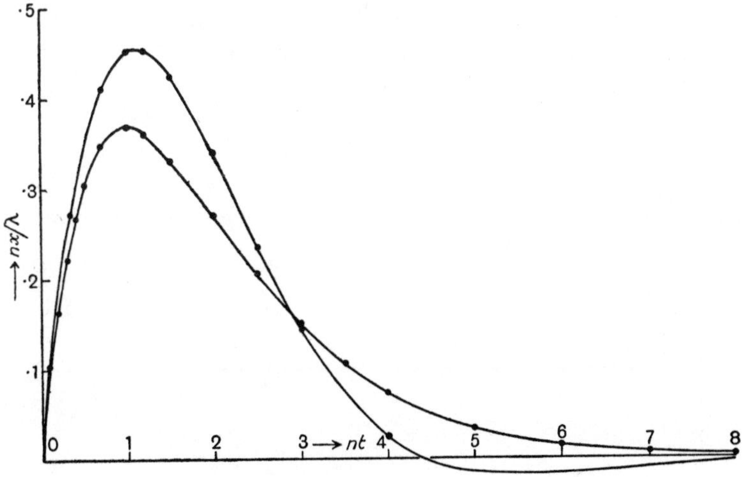

Fig. 4. Recovery of seismographs with $\kappa = n$ and $\kappa = n/\sqrt{2}$ after same impulse.

and the motion does not die down so rapidly as for $\kappa = n$. The aperiodic state therefore gives the least motion after a long interval for a given value of n.

In practice, however, κ is usually made rather less than n; in the Milne-Shaw machine, for instance, κ is about $0{\cdot}7n$. The motion is then oscillatory, but the ratio of the first swing to the second is $e^{\kappa\pi/\gamma}$, or about 20. But x vanishes after an interval π/γ from the start, or about $4/n$, and ever afterwards is a small fraction of its first maximum. The reduced damping effect after a long time is considered less important than the quick and complete recovery after the first maximum. The time of the first maximum is $1{\cdot}1/n$ from the start, as against $1/n$ for the aperiodic instrument and $1{\cdot}57/n$ for the undamped one.

3.31. The Galitzin seismograph is similarly arranged, but the motion of the pendulum generates by electromagnetic induction a current, which passes through a galvanometer. If x is the displacement of the pendulum, and y that of the galvanometer, the differential equations are

$$\ddot{x} + 2\kappa_1 \dot{x} + n_1^2 x = \lambda \ddot{\xi}, \qquad \text{.......................(1)}$$

$$\ddot{y} + 2\kappa_2 \dot{y} + n_2^2 y = \mu \dot{x}. \qquad \text{.......................(2)}$$

Supposing the ground again to start suddenly with unit velocity, we have

$$y = \frac{\lambda \mu p^2}{(p^2 + 2\kappa_1 p + n_1^2)(p^2 + 2\kappa_2 p + n_2^2)} H(t). \qquad \text{.........(3)}$$

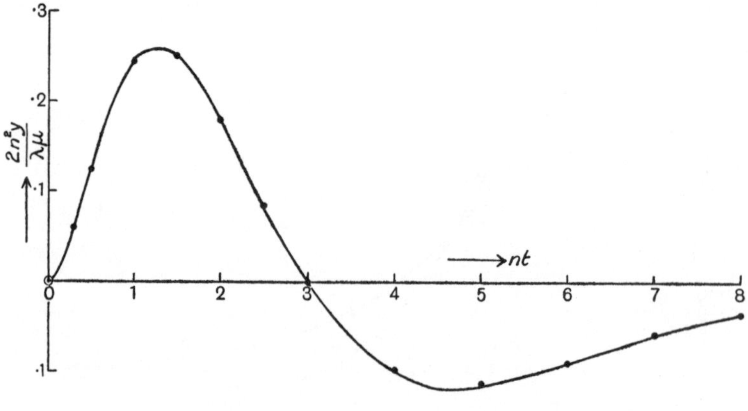

Fig. 5. Recovery of Galitzin seismograph after impulse.

As a rule the two interacting systems are so arranged that κ and n are the same for both, and both are aperiodic, so that $\kappa = n$. Then

$$y = \frac{\lambda\mu p^2}{(p+n)^4} H(t) \qquad \text{.......(4)}$$

$$= \lambda\mu \frac{d}{dt}\left(\frac{t^3}{3!} e^{-nt}\right) \text{ when } t > 0 \qquad \text{.......(5)}$$

$$= \tfrac{1}{2}\lambda\mu\,(t^2 - \tfrac{1}{3}nt^3)\,e^{-nt}. \qquad \text{.......(6)}$$

The indicator therefore begins to move with a finite acceleration, instead of with a finite velocity as for the pendulum. The maximum displacement follows after time $(3-\surd 3)/n = 1{\cdot}27/n$, the mirror passes through the equilibrium position after time $3/n$, and there is a maximum displacement in the opposite direction after time $4{\cdot}73/n$. The mirror then returns asymptotically to the position of equilibrium. The ratio of the two maxima is $e^{2\surd 3}/(2+\surd 3)^2 = 2{\cdot}3$. In comparison with an instrument such as the Milne-Shaw, recording the displacement of the pendulum directly, the Galitzin machine gives the first maximum a little later, the first zero a little earlier, and the next maximum displacement is larger in comparison with the first maximum.

In an actual earthquake the velocity of the ground is annulled by other waves arriving later; the complete motion of the seismograph is a combination of those given by the separate displacements of the ground.

3.4. *Resonance.* A simple pendulum, originally hanging in equilibrium, is disturbed for a finite time by a force varying harmonically in a period equal to the free period of the pendulum. Find the motion after the force is removed.

The differential equation is

$$\ddot{x} + n^2 x = f \sin nt \qquad \text{.......(1)}$$

$$= f\frac{np}{p^2+n^2}. \qquad \text{.......(2)}$$

The solution is then

$$x = f\frac{np}{(p^2+n^2)^2}, \qquad \text{.......(3)}$$

nothing having to be added on account of the initial conditions.

To evaluate this, we notice that

$$\frac{p}{p^2+n^2} = \frac{1}{n}\sin nt. \qquad \text{.......(4)}$$

Differentiating with regard to n, we have

$$-\frac{2np}{(p^2+n^2)^2}=\frac{1}{n}t\cos nt-\frac{1}{n^2}\sin nt, \quad \text{......(5)}$$

and

$$x=\frac{f}{2n^2}(\sin nt-nt\cos nt). \quad \text{......(6)}$$

Suppose the disturbance acts for time $r\pi/n$, where r is an integer. At the end of this time

$$x=-\frac{f}{2n^2}r\pi(-1)^r;\ \dot{x}=0. \quad \text{......(7)}$$

The subsequent motion is therefore given by

$$x=-\frac{(-1)^r r\pi f}{2n^2}\cos(nt-r\pi)$$

$$=-\frac{r\pi f}{2n^2}\cos nt. \quad \text{......(8)}$$

3.5. Three particles of masses m, $\frac{21}{20}m$, and m, in order, are attached to a light stretched string, the ends of the string being fixed. One of the particles of mass m is struck by a transverse impulse I. Find the subsequent motion of the middle particle. (Intercollegiate Examination, 1923.)

If x_1, x_2, x_3 are the displacements of the three particles, P the tension, and l the distance between consecutive particles, we find in the usual way the three equations of motion

$$\ddot{x}_1=-\lambda(2x_1-x_2), \quad \text{......(1)}$$

$$\tfrac{21}{20}\ddot{x}_2=-\lambda(-x_1+2x_2-x_3), \quad \text{......(2)}$$

$$\ddot{x}_3=-\lambda(-x_2+2x_3), \quad \text{......(3)}$$

where

$$\lambda=\frac{P}{ml}. \quad \text{......(4)}$$

Initially all the displacements are zero, $\dot{x}_2=\dot{x}_3=0$, $\dot{x}_1=I/m$. Hence the subsidiary equations are

$$(p^2+2\lambda)x_1-\lambda x_2=pI/m, \quad \text{......(5)}$$

$$-\lambda x_1+(\tfrac{21}{20}p^2+2\lambda)x_2-\lambda x_3=0, \quad \text{......(6)}$$

$$-\lambda x_2+(p^2+2\lambda)x_3=0. \quad \text{......(7)}$$

Hence

$$x_3=\frac{\lambda}{p^2+2\lambda}x_2;\ x_1=\frac{\lambda}{p^2+2\lambda}x_2+\frac{p}{p^2+2\lambda}\frac{I}{m}, \quad \text{......(8)}$$

and

$$\left(\frac{21}{20}p^2+2\lambda-\frac{2\lambda^2}{p^2+2\lambda}\right)x_2=\frac{\lambda p}{p^2+2\lambda}\frac{I}{m}. \quad \text{......(9)}$$

Multiplying by $p^2+2\lambda$ we find

$$(7p^2+4\lambda)(3p^2+10\lambda)x_2=20\lambda pI/m, \quad \text{......(10)}$$

and
$$x_2 = \frac{20\lambda p}{(7p^2+4\lambda)(3p^2+10\lambda)}\frac{I}{m}$$
$$= \frac{20}{58}\frac{I}{m}\left\{\frac{7p}{7p^2+4\lambda} - \frac{3p}{3p^2+10\lambda}\right\}$$
$$= \frac{10}{29}\frac{I}{m}\left\{\frac{\sin\alpha t}{\alpha} - \frac{\sin\beta t}{\beta}\right\}, \quad \text{.....................(11)}$$

where
$$\alpha^2 = \tfrac{4}{7}\lambda; \quad \beta^2 = \tfrac{10}{3}\lambda. \quad \text{.....................(12)}$$

We notice that the mode of speed $\surd(2\lambda)$ is excited, but does not need to be evaluated because it does not affect the middle particle.

3.6. *Radioactive Disintegration of Uranium.* The uranium family of elements are such that an atom of any one of them, except the last, is capable of breaking up into an atom of the next and an atom of helium*. The helium atom undergoes no further change. The number of atoms of any element in a given specimen that break up in a short interval of time is proportional to the time interval and to the number of atoms of that element present. If then $u, x_1, x_2, \ldots x_n$ are the numbers of atoms of the various elements present at time t, they will satisfy the differential equations

$$\left.\begin{aligned} \frac{du}{dt} &= -\kappa u, \\ \frac{dx_1}{dt} &= \kappa u - \kappa_1 x_1, \\ \frac{dx_2}{dt} &= \kappa_1 x_1 - \kappa_2 x_2, \\ &\cdots\cdots\cdots\cdots \\ \frac{dx_n}{dt} &= \kappa_{n-1} x_{n-1}. \end{aligned}\right\} \quad \text{.....................(1)}$$

Suppose that initially only uranium is present. Thus when $t=0$, $u=u_0$, and all the other dependent variables are zero. Then the subsidiary equations are

$$\left.\begin{aligned} (p+\kappa)\,u &= pu_0, \\ (p+\kappa_1)\,x_1 &= \kappa u, \\ (p+\kappa_2)\,x_2 &= \kappa_1 x_1, \\ &\cdots\cdots\cdots\cdots \\ (p+\kappa_{n-1})\,x_{n-1} &= \kappa_{n-2} x_{n-2}, \\ px_n &= \kappa_{n-1} x_{n-1}. \end{aligned}\right\} \quad \text{.................(2)}$$

* We neglect β-ray products, for reasons that will appear later.

The operational solutions are

$$\left.\begin{aligned} u &= \frac{pu_0}{p+\kappa};\ x_1 = \frac{\kappa p u_0}{(p+\kappa)(p+\kappa_1)};\\ x_2 &= \frac{\kappa\kappa_1 p u_0}{(p+\kappa)(p+\kappa_1)(p+\kappa_2)};\\ &\dots\dots\dots\dots\dots\dots\\ x_n &= \frac{\kappa\kappa_1 \dots \kappa_{n-1} u_0}{(p+\kappa)(p+\kappa_1)\dots(p+\kappa_{n-1})}. \end{aligned}\right\} \quad \dots\dots(3)$$

These are directly adapted for interpretation by the partial-fraction rule. In fact

$$\left.\begin{aligned} &u = u_0 e^{-\kappa t};\ x_1 = \frac{\kappa u_0}{\kappa_1 - \kappa}\left(e^{-\kappa t} - e^{-\kappa_1 t}\right);\\ &x_2 = \kappa\kappa_1 u_0 \left\{\frac{1}{(\kappa_1-\kappa)(\kappa_2-\kappa)} e^{-\kappa t} + \frac{1}{(\kappa-\kappa_1)(\kappa_2-\kappa_1)} e^{-\kappa_1 t}\right.\\ &\qquad\qquad \left. + \frac{1}{(\kappa-\kappa_2)(\kappa_1-\kappa_2)} e^{-\kappa_2 t}\right\};\\ &\dots\dots\dots\dots\dots\dots\\ &x_n = u_0 - \frac{\kappa_1 \dots \kappa_{n-1} u_0}{(\kappa_1-\kappa)\dots(\kappa_{n-1}-\kappa)} e^{-\kappa t} - \dots. \end{aligned}\right\} \quad \dots(4)$$

Of all the decay constants κ is much the smallest. If the time elapsed is long enough for all the exponential functions except $e^{-\kappa t}$ to have become insignificant, these results reduce approximately to

$$u = u_0 e^{-\kappa t};\ x_1 = \frac{\kappa}{\kappa_1} u_0 e^{-\kappa t};\ x_2 = \frac{\kappa}{\kappa_2} u_0 e^{-\kappa t};\ \dots\ x_n = u_0\left(1 - e^{-\kappa t}\right). \quad \dots(5)$$

With the exception of the last, the quantities of the various elements decrease, retaining constant ratios to one another.

On the other hand, if the time elapsed is so short that unity is still a first approximation to all the exponential functions, we can proceed by expanding the operators in descending powers of p and interpreting term by term. Hence we see that at first x_1 will increase in proportion to t, x_2 to t^2, and x_n to t^n.

In experimental work an intermediate condition often occurs. Some of the exponentials may become insignificant in the time occupied by an experiment, while others are still nearly unity. We have

$$x_r = \frac{\kappa_{r-1} x_{r-1}}{p + \kappa_r} = \kappa_{r-1}\left[p^{-1} x_{r-1} - \kappa_r p^{-2} x_{r-1} + \dots\right] \quad \dots\dots\dots(6)$$

and if $\kappa_r t$ is small we can neglect the second and later terms in comparison with the first. Thus in this case

$$x_r = \kappa_{r-1} p^{-1} x_{r-1}. \quad \dots\dots\dots(7)$$

If x_{r-1} is of the form t^s, we can put

$$x_r = \frac{\kappa_{r-1} s!}{(p+\kappa_r)p^s} = \frac{\kappa_{r-1} s!}{p^{s+1}} \frac{p}{p+\kappa_r} = \frac{\kappa_{r-1} s!}{p^{s+1}} e^{-\kappa_r t}. \quad \text{.........(8)}$$

If $\kappa_r t$ is small, we can replace the exponential by unity and confirm (7). If it is great,

$$p^{-1} e^{-\kappa_r t} = \int_0^t e^{-\kappa_r t}\, dt = \frac{1}{\kappa_r} + O(e^{-\kappa_r t}),$$

and on continuing the integrations

$$p^{-s-1} e^{-\kappa_r t} = p^{-s} \frac{1}{\kappa_r} = \frac{1}{\kappa_r} \frac{t^s}{s!}.$$

Thus
$$x_r = \frac{\kappa_{r-1}}{\kappa_r} t^s = \frac{\kappa_{r-1}}{\kappa_r} x_{r-1}. \quad \text{........................(9)}$$

Classifying elements into long-lived and short-lived according as $\kappa_r t$ is small or large for them, we find that the quantity of the first long-lived element after uranium is proportional to t, the next to t^2, and so on. All β-ray products are short-lived when t has ordinary values.

Radium is the third degeneration product of uranium. In rock specimens the time elapsed since formation is usually such that the relations (5) have become established. As a matter of observation the numbers of atoms of radium and uranium are found to be in the constant ratio $3{\cdot}58 \times 10^{-7}$. This determines κ/κ_3. Also the rate of break-up of radium is known directly: in fact

$$1/\kappa_3 = 2280 \text{ years}.$$

Hence
$$1/\kappa = 6{\cdot}37 \times 10^9 \text{ years}.$$

This gives the rate of disintegration of uranium itself.

A number of specimens of uranium compounds were carefully freed from radium by Soddy, and then kept for ten years. It was found that new radium was formed; the amount found varied as the square of the time. This would suggest that of the two elements between uranium and radium in the series one was long-lived and the other short-lived. Actually, however, it is known independently that both are long-lived. The first, however, is chemically inseparable from ordinary uranium, and therefore was present in the original specimens; initially, instead of $x_1 = 0$, we have

$$x_1 = \frac{\kappa}{\kappa_1} u_0.$$

For the next element, ionium, we have

$$x_2 = \kappa_1 p^{-1} x_1 = \kappa u_0 t,$$

the variation of x_1 being inappreciable in the time involved. Also

$$x_3 = \kappa_2 p^{-1} x_2 = \tfrac{1}{2}\kappa\kappa_2 u_0 t^2.$$

Soddy* found that 3 kilograms of uranium in 10·15 years gave 202×10^{-12} gm. of radium. Hence, allowing for the difference of atomic weights,

$$x_3/u_0 = 7{\cdot}1 \times 10^{-14}$$

and $$\kappa_2 = 8{\cdot}64 \times 10^{-6}/\text{year}; \quad 1/\kappa_2 = 1{\cdot}16 \times 10^5 \text{ years}.$$

This gives the rate of degeneration of ionium. Soddy gets a slightly lower value for $1/\kappa_2$ from more numerous data.

3.7. *Small Oscillations in Dynamics.* Suppose that we have a dynamical system in equilibrium or steady motion, with a Routh's modified Lagrangian function of the form

$$2R = a_{rs}\dot{x}_r\dot{x}_s + g_{rs}x_r\dot{x}_s - c_{rs}x_r x_s, \quad \text{..............(1)}$$

where x_r are the departures of the non-ignorable coordinates from their values in the steady motion. The friction, if any, is represented by a dissipation function F given by

$$2F = f_{rs}\dot{x}_r\dot{x}_s. \quad \text{..............................(2)}$$

By symmetry there is no loss of generality in taking

$$a_{rs} = a_{sr}; \quad c_{rs} = c_{sr}; \quad f_{rs} = f_{sr}. \quad \text{.....................(3)}$$

The equations of motion for small disturbances are

$$\frac{d}{dt}\left(\frac{\partial R}{\partial \dot{x}_r}\right) - \frac{\partial R}{\partial x_r} + \frac{\partial F}{\partial \dot{x}_r} = 0, \quad \text{.....................(4)}$$

that is $$a_{rs}\ddot{x}_s + b_{rs}\dot{x}_s + c_{rs}x_s = 0, \quad \text{.....................(5)}$$

where $$b_{rs} = g_{sr} - g_{rs} + f_{rs}. \quad \text{.......................(6)}$$

If an external force S_r is applied to the coordinate x_r, the equations have the form 1.72 (1). If the system starts from rest and only one of the S_r differs from zero, the subsidiary equations are

$$e_{ms}x_s = 0 \ (m \neq r); \quad e_{ms}x_s = S_r \ (m = r). \quad \text{...........(7)}$$

Writing Δ for the determinant formed by the e's, and E_{rs} for the minor of e_{rs} in this determinant, we have the operational solution

$$x_s = \frac{E_{rs}}{\Delta} S_r. \quad \text{..............................(8)}$$

If all the $b_{rs} = 0$, the determinant Δ is symmetrical, so that

$$E_{rs} = E_{sr}. \quad \text{..............................(9)}$$

* *Phil. Mag.* (6) 38 (1919), 483–488.

Then a given force S_r applied to the coordinate x_r will produce precisely the same variation in x_s as the same force would produce in x_r if it was applied to x_s. Thus we have a reciprocity theorem applicable to all non-gyroscopic and frictionless systems. Friction does not affect the result if it is expressible by a dissipation function F, for $f_{rs}=f_{sr}$ and the relation (9) still holds.

If the forces reduce to an impulse at $t=0$, so that S_r can be replaced by pJ_r, the solution becomes

$$x_s=\frac{E_{rs}}{\Delta}pJ_r. \qquad (10)$$

We can evaluate the initial velocities by expanding in descending powers of p. The first term is

$$x_s=\frac{A_{rs}}{A}\frac{1}{p}J_r, \qquad (11)$$

where A is the determinant formed by the a's, and A_{rs} the minor of a_{rs} in it. Hence the initial velocities, found by operating on this with p, are

$$px_s=\frac{A_{rs}}{A}J_r. \qquad (12)$$

Now the constants a_{rs} are merely twice the coefficients in the kinetic energy, which is a quadratic form. Hence the determinant A is symmetrical whether the system is gyroscopic or not, and the reciprocity theorem for impulses and the velocities produced by them is proved.

3.71. The subsequent motion can be investigated by interpreting according to the partial-fraction rule. But let us consider the simple case where the system is non-gyroscopic and frictionless. Then

$$\Delta=A\Pi(p^2+\alpha^2), \qquad (1)$$

where the α's are the speeds of the normal modes. Then

$$x_s=\Sigma_\alpha\frac{E_{rs}(-\alpha^2)}{\alpha(d\Delta/dp^2)_{p^2=-\alpha^2}}J_r\sin\alpha t, \qquad (2)$$

where $E_{rs}(-\alpha^2)$ denotes the result of putting $-\alpha^2$ for p^2 in E_{rs}. The contribution of the α mode to the initial rate of change of x_s is therefore

$$v_{s\alpha}=\frac{E_{rs}(-\alpha^2)}{(d\Delta/dp^2)_{p^2=-\alpha^2}}J_r. \qquad (3)$$

An immediate consequence of the presence of the factor $E_{rs}(-\alpha^2)$ in the numerator is that if an impulse is applied at a node of any normal mode, that mode will be absent from the motion generated.

Another illustration is provided by Lamb's discussion* of the waves generated in a semi-infinite homogeneous elastic solid by an internal disturbance. The normal modes of such a system include a type of waves known as Rayleigh waves. These may be of any length, and involve both compressional and distortional movement; if the depth is z, the amplitude of the compressional movement in a given wave is proportional to $e^{-\alpha z}$, and that of the distortional movement to $e^{-\beta z}$, where α and β depend only on the wave-length. Lamb found that if the original disturbance was an expansive one at a depth f, the amplitude of the motion at the surface contained a factor $e^{-\alpha f}$; but if the original disturbance was purely distortional, the corresponding amplitude contained a factor $e^{-\beta f}$. These factors are the same as would occur in the compression and distortion respectively at depth f in a Rayleigh wave with given amplitude at the surface.

3.72. In the discussion of the oscillations of dynamical systems about equilibrium the ordinary method of seeking for solutions of the form $x_s = \lambda_s e^{\gamma t}$ meets with a difficulty when the determinantal equation for the periods has equal roots. This does not arise in the present method. If the system is not dissipative and the roots are unequal, we know that the zeros of the minor of any element in the leading diagonal separate those of the original determinant; hence in the limit, if the determinant has a factor $(p^2+\alpha^2)^r$, the minor of any element in the leading diagonal has a factor $(p^2+\alpha^2)^{r-1}$, and therefore every first minor contains this factor. Hence when we evaluate the operational solution for given initial conditions as in 1.72 (7), in the absence of external forces, we shall have

$$x_m = \frac{E_{rm}}{\Delta} a_{rs}(p^2 u_s + p v_s),$$

and the factor $(p^2+\alpha^2)^{r-1}$ cancels from the numerator and denominator of E_{rm}/Δ. Hence only a single factor $(p^2+\alpha^2)$ remains in the denominator, and the corresponding partial fraction contributes only trigonometric terms $\cos \alpha t$ and $\sin \alpha t$ to the solution.

In dissipative or gyroscopic systems, b_{rs} is not zero, and the root-separation theorem may not hold. Then equal roots do not necessarily imply a corresponding factor in E_{rm}, and the operational solution may still have a repeated factor in the denominator. Then terms like $te^{-\alpha t}$, $t \cos \alpha t$, $t \sin \alpha t$ will occur in the solution. A simple instance of this has already appeared in the aperiodic seismograph discussed in 3.3.

* *Phil. Trans.*, A, 203 (1904), 1–42.

CHAPTER IV

WAVE MOTION IN ONE DIMENSION

4.1. In a large class of physical problems we meet with the differential equation

$$\frac{\partial^2 y}{\partial t^2} - c^2 \frac{\partial^2 y}{\partial x^2} = 0, \quad \text{.........................(1)}$$

where t is the time, x the distance from a fixed point or a fixed plane, y the independent variable, and c a known velocity. Let us consider the solution of this equation first with regard to the transverse vibrations of a stretched string. In this case we know that

$$c^2 = P/m, \quad \text{..............................(2)}$$

where P is the tension and m the mass per unit length. Write p for $\partial/\partial t$, and D for $\partial/\partial x$. Suppose that at time zero

$$y = f(x); \quad \frac{\partial y}{\partial t} = F(x), \quad \text{.....................(3)}$$

where f and F are known functions of x; that is, we are given the initial displacement and velocity of the string at all points of its length. Then we are led by our previous rules to consider the subsidiary equation

$$(p^2 - c^2 D^2) y = p^2 f(x) + p\, F(x) \quad \text{..................(4)}$$

or

$$y = \frac{p^2}{p^2 - c^2 D^2} f(x) + \frac{p}{p^2 - c^2 D^2} F(x). \quad \text{..............(5)}$$

But

$$\frac{p^2}{p^2 - c^2 D^2} = \tfrac{1}{2}\left(\frac{p}{p - cD} + \frac{p}{p + cD}\right)$$
$$= \tfrac{1}{2}\left(e^{cDt} + e^{-cDt}\right), \quad \text{........................(6)}$$

$$\frac{p}{p^2 - c^2 D^2} = \frac{1}{2cD}\left(\frac{p}{p - cD} - \frac{p}{p + cD}\right)$$
$$= \frac{1}{2c}\left(e^{cDt} - e^{-cDt}\right)\frac{1}{D}. \quad \text{...................(7)}$$

In (7) the $1/D$ has been put last in consequence of our rule that operations involving negative powers of D must be carried out before those involving positive powers. Hence

$$\frac{p^2}{p^2 - c^2 D^2} f(x) = \tfrac{1}{2}\left(e^{cDt} + e^{-cDt}\right) f(x)$$
$$= \tfrac{1}{2}\{f(x + ct) + f(x - ct)\}, \quad \text{..............(8)}$$

$$\frac{p}{p^2-c^2D^2}F(x)=\frac{1}{2c}(e^{cDt}-e^{-cDt})\int_0^x F(x)\,dx$$
$$=\frac{1}{2c}\left[\int_0^{x+ct} F(x)\,dx-\int_0^{x-ct} F(x)\,dx\right]$$
$$=\frac{1}{2c}\int_{x-ct}^{x+ct} F(x)\,dx \quad\text{......................(9)}$$

and therefore

$$y=\tfrac{1}{2}\{f(x+ct)+f(x-ct)\}+\frac{1}{2c}\int_{x-ct}^{x+ct} F(x)\,dx. \quad\text{......(10)}$$

This is D'Alembert's well-known solution.

This cannot, however, be the complete solution. Equation (1) has been assumed to hold at all points of the string; but if any external forces act these must be included on the right of the equation of motion. In such problems the ends of the string are usually fixed, and reactions at the ends are required to maintain this state; in the complete equations of motion these reactions should appear. They are unknown functions of t, and therefore necessitate a change in the mode of solution. This corresponds to a real indefiniteness in the solution itself; for if the string stretches from $x=0$ to $x=l$, $f(x+ct)$ is unspecified if $x+ct>l$, and $f(x-ct)$ is unspecified if $x-ct$ is negative. The solution is therefore incapable of application to a specific problem unless we can obtain a means of specifying $f(x)$ and $F(x)$ outside the original range.

But D'Alembert's solution can be adapted so as to fulfil all the conditions. We notice that the solution consists of two waves travelling in opposite directions with velocity c. If the initial disturbance is confined to a region within the string separated by finite intervals from both ends, it will take a finite time before D'Alembert's solution gives a displacement at either end; hence no force is required to maintain the boundary conditions, and the solution will hold accurately until one of the waves reaches one end.

Again, the initial disturbance is specified only for points within the length of the string, that is, for values of x between 0 and l, say; and by the last paragraph D'Alembert's solution would be complete if the length were infinite. If then we consider an infinite string stretching from $-\infty$ to $+\infty$, and disturbed initially so that $f(x)$ and $F(x)$ are both antisymmetrical about both $x=0$ and $x=l$, y will vanish ever after at these points, so that no force is required to keep them fixed, and D'Alembert's solution for such an infinite string will therefore be equivalent to that for the actual string from $x=0$ to $x=l$. Thus we have a formal rule for finding the position of the string at any subsequent time: consider an infinite string with the actual values of the initial velocity and displacement between $x=0$ and $x=l$, but with the displacement and velocity outside this stretch so specified as to be antisymmetrical with regard to both $x=0$ and $x=l$; then D'Alembert's solution for the infinite string will be correct for the actual string for the same values of x.

4.2. We may approach the problem in another way. Taking the same subsidiary equation

$$\frac{\partial^2 y}{\partial x^2}-\frac{p^2}{c^2}y=-\frac{p^2}{c^2}f(x), \qquad \text{(1)}$$

except that the effects of the initial velocity will not be considered at present, let us solve with regard to x as if p were a constant. The justification of this procedure is that $\partial/\partial x$ is commutative with regard to both differentiation and integration with regard to t. The boundary conditions are that $y=0$ when $x=0$ and when $x=l$. Using the method of variation of parameters, we assume that the solution is

$$y=A\cosh\frac{px}{c}+B\sinh\frac{px}{c}, \qquad \text{(2)}$$

where A and B are functions of x subject to

$$A'\cosh\frac{px}{c}+B'\sinh\frac{px}{c}=0. \qquad \text{(3)}$$

Substituting in the equation (1) we find

$$A'\sinh\frac{px}{c}+B'\cosh\frac{px}{c}=-\frac{p}{c}f(x). \qquad \text{(4)}$$

Hence

$$A'=\frac{p}{c}f(x)\sinh\frac{px}{c}\,;\quad B'=-\frac{p}{c}f(x)\cosh\frac{px}{c}. \qquad \text{(5)}$$

Now y must vanish for all time when $x=0$; hence $A(0)=0$. Thus

$$A=\int_0^x\frac{p}{c}f(\xi)\sinh\frac{p\xi}{c}\,d\xi. \qquad \text{(6)}$$

Also y must vanish when $x=l$. Hence

$$B(l)\sinh\frac{pl}{c}=-A(l)\cosh\frac{pl}{c} \qquad \text{(7)}$$

and

$$B(l)=-\coth\frac{pl}{c}\int_0^l\frac{p}{c}f(\xi)\sinh\frac{p\xi}{c}\,d\xi, \qquad \text{(8)}$$

giving

$$B(x)=-\coth\frac{pl}{c}\int_0^l\frac{p}{c}f(\xi)\sinh\frac{p\xi}{c}\,d\xi+\int_x^l\frac{p}{c}f(\xi)\cosh\frac{p\xi}{c}\,d\xi. \qquad \text{(9)}$$

In all we find

$$y = \int_0^x \frac{p}{c} f(\xi) \sinh \frac{p\xi}{c} \left(\cosh \frac{px}{c} - \coth \frac{pl}{c} \sinh \frac{px}{c}\right) d\xi$$
$$+ \int_x^l \frac{p}{c} f(\xi) \sinh \frac{px}{c} \left(\cosh \frac{p\xi}{c} - \coth \frac{pl}{c} \sinh \frac{p\xi}{c}\right) d\xi$$
$$= \int_0^x \frac{p}{c} f(\xi) \sinh \frac{p\xi}{c} \frac{\sinh p(l-x)/c}{\sinh pl/c} d\xi$$
$$+ \int_x^l \frac{p}{c} f(\xi) \sinh \frac{px}{c} \frac{\sinh p(l-\xi)/c}{\sinh pl/c} d\xi. \quad \text{.................(10)}$$

Before carrying out the integration with regard to ξ, we can interpret the integrand by the partial-fraction rule. Each integral vanishes when $p=0$, and therefore no constant term appears in the solution. But $\sinh pl/c$ vanishes when

$$\frac{pl}{c} = r\iota\pi, \quad \text{..............................(11)}$$

where r is any integer, positive or negative. Hence

$$\frac{p}{c} \sinh \frac{p\xi}{c} \frac{\sinh p(l-x)/c}{\sinh pl/c} = \sum_{r=-\infty}^{r=\infty} \frac{\frac{r\iota\pi}{l} \sinh \frac{r\iota\pi\xi}{l} \sinh r\iota\pi \frac{l-x}{l}}{\frac{cr\iota\pi}{l} \cosh (r\iota\pi) \frac{l}{c}} e^{r\iota\pi ct/l}$$
$$= \sum_{r=1}^{\infty} \frac{2}{l} \sin \frac{r\pi\xi}{l} \sin \frac{r\pi x}{l} \cos \frac{r\pi ct}{l}. \quad \text{.........(12)}$$

By symmetry the corresponding factor in the second integral has the same value. Hence

$$y = \sum_{r=1}^{\infty} \frac{2}{l} \int_0^l f(\xi) \sin \frac{r\pi\xi}{l} d\xi \,.\, \sin \frac{r\pi x}{l} \cos \frac{r\pi ct}{l}. \quad \text{.....(13)}$$

This is the solution given by the method of normal coordinates. Putting t zero, we obtain the Fourier sine series

$$f(x) = \sum_{r=1}^{\infty} \frac{2}{l} \int_0^l f(\xi) \sin \frac{r\pi\xi}{l} \sin \frac{r\pi x}{l} d\xi. \quad \text{...............(14)}$$

The effect of an initial velocity can be obtained by a similar process.

But in practice the solution by trigonometrical series is not often the most convenient form unless we are satisfied with a knowledge of the free periods. It usually converges slowly; but what is more serious is that its form suggests little about the nature of the actual motion beyond the fact that it is periodic in time $2l/c$. To find the actual form of the string at any instant it is necessary to find some way of summing the series, which may be rather difficult. A more convenient method is often the following*. We have seen that the interpretation of

* Heaviside, *Electromagnetic Theory*, 2, 108–114.

any operator valid for positive values of the argument is equivalent to an integral in the complex plane, the path of integration being on the positive side of the imaginary axis. Then a factor cosech pl/c in the operator can be written

$$\frac{1}{\sinh pl/c} = \frac{2e^{-pl/c}}{1-e^{-2pl/c}} = 2e^{-pl/c}\left(1+e^{-2pl/c}+e^{-4pl/c}+\ldots\right) \quad \ldots(15)$$

and when interpreted by Bromwich's rule this will give rise to a series in powers of $e^{-2\lambda l/c}$ in the integrand. But since the real part of λ is everywhere positive on the path, the series is absolutely convergent, and integration term by term is justified. Hence it is legitimate to expand the operator in this way and to interpret term by term. Then for $\xi < x$,

$$\frac{\sinh p\xi/c \sinh p(l-x)/c}{\sinh pl/c} = \tfrac{1}{2}e^{-p(x-\xi)/c}\left(1-e^{-2p\xi/c}\right)$$
$$\left(1-e^{-2p(l-x)/c}\right)\left(1+e^{-2pl/c}+e^{-4pl/c}+\ldots\right); \quad \ldots(16)$$

and for $\xi > x$,

$$\frac{\sinh px/c \sinh p(l-\xi)/c}{\sinh pl/c} = \tfrac{1}{2}e^{-p(\xi-x)/c}\left(1-e^{-2px/c}\right)$$
$$\left(1-e^{-2p(l-\xi)/c}\right)\left(1+e^{-2pl/c}+e^{-4pl/c}+\ldots\right). \quad \ldots(17)$$

On multiplying out either expression we obtain a series of negative exponentials of the forms $e^{-p(a-\xi)/c}$, with $a > \xi$, or $e^{-p(\xi-a)/c}$, with $\xi > a$.

Then $$\int_{\xi_1}^{\xi_2} \frac{p}{c} f(\xi)\, e^{-p(a-\xi)/c}\, d\xi = \int f(\xi)\, de^{-p(a-\xi)/c}. \quad \ldots\ldots\ldots(18)$$

But according to our rule $e^{-p(a-\xi)/c}$ is zero when $t-(a-\xi)/c$ is negative and unity when this quantity is positive. Hence the integral (18) is zero unless $a-ct$ lies between ξ_1 and ξ_2, and then it is equal to $f(a-ct)$.

Similarly $$\int_{\xi_1}^{\xi_2} \frac{p}{c} f(\xi)\, e^{-p(\xi-a)/c}\, d\xi = -\int f(\xi)\, de^{-p(\xi-a)/c} \quad \ldots\ldots(19)$$

and $$e^{-p(\xi-a)/c} = 0 \text{ if } \xi > ct+a$$
$$= 1 \text{ if } \xi < ct+a,$$

so that (19) is zero unless $ct+a$ lies between ξ_1 and ξ_2, and then is equal to $f(ct+a)$.

It follows that at any instant the effect of the initial displacement $f(\xi)$ at the point ξ is zero except at a special set of points where one or other of the quantities $a \pm ct$ is equal to ξ. Since a does not involve ξ, we see that this way of expressing the solution reduces it to a set of waves moving in each direction with velocity c. The first three factors in (16) give

$$\tfrac{1}{2}\{e^{-p(x-\xi)/c}-e^{-p(x+\xi)/c}-e^{-p\{(x-\xi)+2(l-x)\}/c}+e^{-p\{(x+\xi)+2(l-x)\}/c}\} \quad\ldots\ldots(20)$$

for values of x greater than ξ. The first term gives $\frac{1}{2}f(\xi)$ at time $(x-\xi)/c$, the second $-\frac{1}{2}f(\xi)$ at time $(x+\xi)/c$, the third $-\frac{1}{2}f(\xi)$ at time $\{x-\xi+2(l-x)\}/c$ and the fourth $\frac{1}{2}f(\xi)$ at time $\{x+\xi+2(l-x)\}/c$. The first term represents the direct wave from ξ to x, the second the wave reflected at $x=0$, the third that reflected at $x=l$, and the fourth one reflected first at $x=0$ and then again at $x=l$. The term $e^{-2pl/c}$ in the last factor of (16) will give four further and similar pulses, each later by $2l/c$ than the corresponding pulse just found. These are pulses that have travelled twice more along the string, having been reflected once more at each end. Similarly we can proceed to the interpretation of later terms as pulses that have undergone still more reflexions.

The part of the solution arising from values of ξ greater than x may be treated similarly. The interpretation in terms of waves is exactly the same.

4.3. As a particular case let us consider a string of length l, originally drawn aside a distance η at the point $x=b$, so that initially it lies in two straight pieces, and then released. Then

$$\left.\begin{aligned} y_0 &= \eta x/b & 0\leqslant x\leqslant b \\ y_0 &= \eta(l-x)/(l-b) & b\leqslant x\leqslant l \end{aligned}\right\} \quad\ldots\ldots\ldots\ldots\ldots(1)$$

and the subsidiary equation is

$$\frac{\partial^2 y}{\partial x^2}-\frac{p^2}{c^2}y=-\frac{p^2}{c^2}y_0. \quad\ldots\ldots\ldots\ldots\ldots\ldots\ldots\ldots(2)$$

The solution that vanishes at the ends is

$$\left.\begin{aligned} y &= \eta\frac{x}{b}+A\sinh\frac{px}{c}\sinh\frac{p}{c}(l-b) & 0\leqslant x\leqslant b \\ y &= \eta\frac{l-x}{l-b}+A\sinh\frac{pb}{c}\sinh\frac{p}{c}(l-x) & b\leqslant x\leqslant l \end{aligned}\right\}, \quad\ldots\ldots(3)$$

where the constants have been chosen so as to make y continuous at $x=b$. Also a discontinuity in $\partial y/\partial x$ at this point would imply an infinite acceleration, which cannot persist. Hence we add the condition that $\partial y/\partial x$ shall be continuous, which gives

$$\eta\left(\frac{1}{b}+\frac{1}{l-b}\right)+\frac{pA}{c}\left\{\cosh\frac{pb}{c}\sinh\frac{p}{c}(l-b)+\sinh\frac{pb}{c}\cosh\frac{p}{c}(l-b)\right\}=0 \quad\ldots\ldots\ldots(4)$$

and on simplifying

$$A = -\frac{c}{p}\frac{l}{b(l-b)}\eta \operatorname{cosech}\frac{pl}{c}. \quad \text{..................(5)}$$

Thus

$$\left.\begin{aligned} y &= \frac{\eta l}{b(l-b)}\left\{\frac{l-b}{l}x - \frac{c}{p}\frac{\sinh px/c \sinh p(l-b)/c}{\sinh pl/c}\right\} \quad 0 \leqslant x \leqslant b \\ y &= \frac{\eta l}{b(l-b)}\left\{\frac{b}{l}(l-x) - \frac{c}{p}\frac{\sinh pb/c \sinh p(l-x)/c}{\sinh pl/c}\right\} \quad b \leqslant x \leqslant l \end{aligned}\right\} \text{. ...(6)}$$

Interpreting by the partial-fraction rule, we notice that the contribution from $p = 0$ just cancels the term independent of p, while the rest gives*

$$y = \frac{2\eta l^2}{b(l-b)}\sum_{r=1}^{\infty}\frac{1}{r^2\pi^2}\sin\frac{r\pi b}{l}\sin\frac{r\pi x}{l}\cos\frac{r\pi ct}{l} \quad 0 \leqslant x \leqslant l. \quad (7)$$

Alternatively, we can interpret the solution for $0 < x < b$ in exponentials, for

$$\frac{\sinh px/c \sinh p(l-b)/c}{\sinh pl/c} = \tfrac{1}{2}e^{-p(b-x)/c}(1 - e^{-2px/c})$$
$$(1 - e^{-2p(l-b)/c})(1 + e^{-2pl/c} + e^{-4pl/c} + \ldots) \text{...(8)}$$

and

$$\frac{c}{p} = ct \quad t > 0. \quad \text{..............................(9)}$$

Then

$$e^{-p(b-x)/c}\frac{c}{p} = ct - (b-x), \quad \text{.....................(10)}$$

when the right side is positive, and otherwise is zero. Thus y retains its initial value $\eta x/l$ unaltered until time $(b-x)/c$, when the wave from the part where $x > b$ begins to arrive. After that we shall have

$$y = \frac{\eta l}{b(l-b)}\left\{\frac{l-b}{l}x - \tfrac{1}{2}(ct - b + x)\right\} = \frac{\eta l}{b(l-b)}\left\{\left(\frac{1}{2} - \frac{b}{l}\right)x - \tfrac{1}{2}(ct-b)\right\}.$$
$$\text{.........(11)}$$

This solution remains correct until $ct = b + x$, when the wave reflected at $x = 0$ begins to arrive. Thenceforward

$$(e^{-p(b-x)/c} - e^{-p(b+x)/c})\frac{c}{p} = \{ct - (b-x)\} - \{ct - (b+x)\} = 2x. \quad \text{...(12)}$$

Hence

$$y = \frac{\eta l}{b(l-b)}\left(\frac{l-b}{l}x - x\right) = -\frac{\eta x}{l-b}. \quad \text{...........(13)}$$

The part of the string reached by the first reflected wave is therefore parallel to the original position of the part where $b < x < l$.

* Rayleigh, *Theory of Sound*, 1, 1894, 185.

When $ct = (b-x) + 2(l-b)$, a wave reflected at $x = l$ arrives, and

$$y = \frac{\eta l}{b(l-b)}\left\{\left(\frac{1}{2}-\frac{b}{l}\right)x + \tfrac{1}{2}(ct+b) - l\right\}. \quad \text{.........(14)}$$

This holds until $ct = (b+x) + 2(l-b)$; in the next phase

$$y = \frac{\eta l}{b(l-b)}x\left(1-\frac{b}{l}\right) = \frac{\eta x}{b}. \quad \text{..................(15)}$$

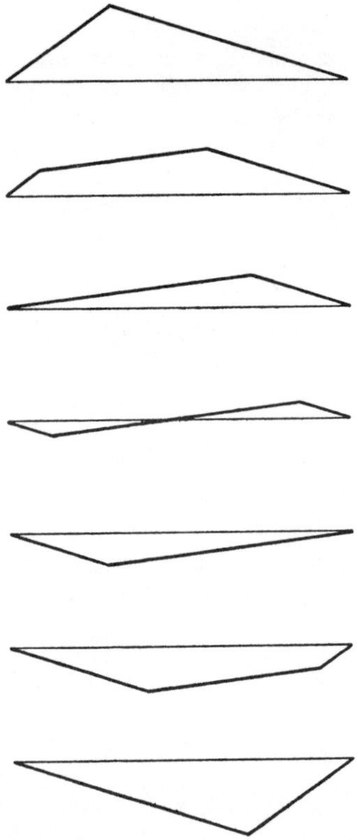

Fig. 6.

When $ct = 2l$, the whole of the string is back in its original position; the term in $e^{-2pl/c}$ then begins to affect the motion, and the whole process repeats itself. We see that at any instant the string is in three straight pieces. The two end pieces are parallel to the two portions of the string in its initial position, and are at rest. For the middle portion the gradient $\partial y/\partial x$ is the mean of those for the end portions, and the transverse velocity is $\pm\frac{1}{2}\frac{\eta l c}{b(l-b)}$. The middle portion is always either extending or withdrawing at each end with velocity c. (Fig. 6.)

4.4. A uniform heavy string of length $2l$ is fixed at the ends. A particle of mass m is attached to the middle of the string. Initially the string is straight. An impulse J is given to the particle. Find the subsequent motion of the particle. (Cf. Rayleigh, *Theory of Sound*, 1, 1894, 204.)

The differential equation of the motion of the string is

$$\frac{\partial^2 y}{\partial t^2}-c^2\frac{\partial^2 y}{\partial x^2}=0. \quad\text{.........................(1)}$$

Take x zero at the middle of the string. By symmetry we need consider only the range of values $0 \leqslant x \leqslant l$. Suppose that the displacement of the particle is η. When $t=0$, y and $\partial y/\partial t$ are zero except at $x=0$. The subsidiary equation therefore needs no additional terms. The solution is therefore

$$y=\eta\frac{\sinh p(l-x)/c}{\sinh pl/c}. \quad\text{.......................(2)}$$

If now P be the tension in the string, the equation of motion of the particle is

$$m\frac{\partial^2 \eta}{\partial t^2}=2P\left(\frac{\partial y}{\partial x}\right)_{x=0}. \quad\text{.......................(3)}$$

If ρ be the mass of the string per unit length,

$$P=\rho c^2. \quad\text{.............................(4)}$$

On account of the initial conditions the subsidiary equation for the particle is

$$mp^2\eta=2P\left(\frac{\partial y}{\partial x}\right)_{x=0}+Jp$$

$$=-2P\eta\frac{p}{c}\coth\frac{pl}{c}+Jp. \quad\text{..............(5)}$$

Hence $$\eta=\frac{Jc}{mpc+2P\coth pl/c}. \quad\text{..............(6)}$$

Put $$\frac{2\rho l}{m}=k=\frac{\text{mass of the string}}{\text{mass of the particle}}. \quad\text{..............(7)}$$

Then $$2P=kmc^2/l \quad\text{..................................(8)}$$

and $$\eta=\frac{lJ/mc}{(pl/c)+k\coth(pl/c)}. \quad\text{...........(9)}$$

To interpret this solution by the partial-fraction rule, we recollect that the system is a stable one without dissipation, and therefore all the zeros of the denominator are purely imaginary. Putting

$$pl/c = \iota\omega \qquad \text{.............................(10)}$$

we see that the zeros are the roots of

$$\omega = k \cot \omega. \qquad \text{.............................(11)}$$

There is a root between every two consecutive multiples of π, positive or negative; and the roots occur in pairs, each pair being numerically equal but opposite in sign. Then

$$\eta = \frac{lJ}{mc} \Sigma \frac{l}{\iota\omega c\,(1 + k\,\operatorname{cosec}^2 \omega)\,(l/c)} e^{\iota\omega ct/l}, \qquad \text{...........(12)}$$

the summation extending over all positive and negative values of ω,

$$= \frac{2lJ}{mc} \Sigma \frac{1}{\omega\,(1 + k\,\operatorname{cosec}^2 \omega)} \sin(\omega ct/l), \qquad \text{...........(13)}$$

the summation being now over positive values of ω.

If a root of (11) is $n\pi + \lambda$, where n is great and $\lambda < \pi$, we have

$$(n\pi + \lambda) \tan \lambda = k \qquad \text{........................(14)}$$

and

$$\lambda = k/n\pi \text{...............................(15)}$$

approximately. The series (13) converges like $\Sigma \frac{1}{\omega} \sin^2 \omega$, or $\Sigma \frac{1}{n^3}$. It therefore converges fairly rapidly at the beginning, but more slowly later. Also the ω's are incommensurable, and therefore the motion does not repeat itself after a finite time; thus the labour of computation would be great.

To express the solution in terms of waves, it is convenient to change the unit of time to l/c, the time a wave takes to traverse half the length of the string. Also J/m may be replaced by V. Then

$$\eta = \frac{V}{p + k \coth p} = \frac{V(1 - e^{-2p})}{(p + k) - (p - k)\,e^{-2p}}$$

$$= V \frac{1 - e^{-2p}}{p + k} \left\{1 + \frac{p - k}{p + k} e^{-2p} + \left(\frac{p - k}{p + k}\right)^2 e^{-4p} + \dots\right\}$$

$$= \frac{V}{p + k} \left(1 - \frac{2k}{p + k} e^{-2p} - \frac{2k\,(p - k)}{(p + k)^2} e^{-4p} - \dots\right). \qquad \text{......(16)}$$

The first term is zero for negative values of the time; for positive values it is equal to

$$\frac{V}{k}(1 - e^{-kt}). \qquad \text{..........................(17)}$$

After time 2 the second term no longer vanishes. We have

$$\frac{k}{(p+k)^2} = \frac{1}{k} - \frac{p}{k(p+k)} - \frac{p}{(p+k)^2}$$

$$= \frac{1}{k} - \frac{1}{k}e^{-kt} - te^{-kt} \quad \text{......................(18)}$$

and the second term is equivalent to

$$-\frac{2V}{k}\{1 - e^{-k(t-2)} - k(t-2)e^{-k(t-2)}\} \text{ for } t > 2. \text{ ....(19)}$$

The third term is zero for $t < 4$; for greater values it is easily found to be

$$\frac{2V}{k}[1 - \{1 + k(t-4) + k^2(t-4)^2\}e^{-k(t-4)}]. \quad \text{.........(20)}$$

The process may be extended to determine the motion up to any instant desired. The entry of a new term into the solution corresponds to the arrival of a new wave reflected at the ends.

4.5. A uniform heavy bar is hanging vertically from one end, and a mass m is suddenly attached at the lower end. Find how the tension at the upper end varies with the time. (Love, *Elasticity*, § 283.)

If x be the distance from the upper end, and y the longitudinal displacement, y satisfies the differential equation

$$\rho\frac{\partial^2 y}{\partial t^2} - E\frac{\partial^2 y}{\partial x^2} = F, \quad \text{........................(1)}$$

where ρ is the density, E Young's modulus, and F the external force per unit volume, in this case ρg. Put $E/\rho = c^2$, and let the displacement of a particle before the weight is attached be y_0. Then

$$-c^2\frac{\partial^2 y_0}{\partial x^2} = g. \quad \text{..........................(2)}$$

When $x = 0$, $y_0 = 0$; and if the bar be of length l, $\partial y_0/\partial x = 0$ when $x = l$.

Hence $$y_0 = \frac{glx}{c^2}\left(1 - \frac{1}{2}\frac{x}{l}\right). \quad \text{........................(3)}$$

After the weight is attached, we still have

$$\frac{\partial^2 y}{\partial t^2} - c^2\frac{\partial^2 y}{\partial x^2} = g = -c^2\frac{\partial^2 y_0}{\partial x^2}, \text{ ....(4)}$$

while when $t = 0$, $y = y_0$ and $\partial y/\partial t = 0$. Hence the subsidiary equation is

$$p^2 y - c^2\frac{\partial^2 y}{\partial x^2} = p^2 y_0 - c^2\frac{\partial^2 y_0}{\partial x^2}, \quad \text{.................(5)}$$

and the solution that vanishes with x is given by

$$y-y_0=A\sinh px/c, \qquad\qquad (6)$$

where A is independent of x.

If ϖ be the cross section of the bar, the equation of motion of the mass m is

$$m\frac{\partial^2 y}{\partial t^2}=mg-E\varpi\frac{\partial y}{\partial x}, \qquad\qquad (7)$$

the derivatives being evaluated at $x=l$. The subsidiary equation is

$$mp^2y=mg+mp^2y_0-E\varpi\frac{\partial y}{\partial x}, \qquad\qquad (8)$$

which gives on substituting for y from (6)

$$\left(p^2\sinh\frac{pl}{c}+\frac{E\varpi p}{mc}\cosh\frac{pl}{c}\right)A=g. \qquad\qquad (9)$$

The tension at the upper end is

$$g\rho l+EpA/c=g\rho l+\frac{Emg}{E\varpi\cosh(pl/c)+mcp\sinh(pl/c)}. \qquad (10)$$

If k be the ratio of the mass of the weight to that of the bar,

$$k=\frac{m}{\rho\varpi l};\ \frac{mc}{E\varpi}=k\frac{l}{c}; \qquad\qquad (11)$$

and the tension is

$$\frac{gm}{\varpi}\left[\frac{1}{k}+\frac{1}{\cosh(pl/c)+k(pl/c)\sinh pl/c}\right]. \qquad\qquad (12)$$

We see that $gm/\varpi k$ is the tension due to the weight of the bar alone, and gm/ϖ is the statical tension due to the added load alone. To evaluate the actual tension, we expand the operator in (12) in powers of $e^{-pl/c}$. Taking l/c for the new unit of time, we have

$$\frac{1}{kp\sinh p+\cosh p}=\frac{2e^{-p}}{(kp+1)-(kp-1)e^{-2p}}$$
$$=\frac{2e^{-p}}{kp+1}\left[1+\frac{kp-1}{kp+1}e^{-2p}+\left(\frac{kp-1}{kp+1}\right)^2e^{-4p}+\dots\right]. \qquad\qquad (13)$$

The first term vanishes up to time unity, and afterwards is equal to

$$2(1-e^{-(t-1)/k}). \qquad\qquad (14)$$

This increases steadily up to time 3, when the next term enters. Again,

$$\frac{kp-1}{(kp+1)^2}=-1+\frac{kp}{kp+1}+\frac{2kp}{(kp+1)^2}$$
$$=-1+e^{-t/k}+2(t/k)e^{-t/k} \qquad\qquad (15)$$

and the first two terms, when $t > 3$, are equivalent to

$$2\,(1 - e^{-(t-1)/k}) - 2\,[1 - e^{-(t-3)/k} - 2\,\{(t-3)/k\}\,e^{-(t-3)/k}]$$
$$= 2e^{-(t-3)/k}\,[1 + (2/k)\,(t-3) - e^{-2/k}]. \quad \text{.................. (16)}$$

This has a maximum when

$$1 + e^{-2/k} = \frac{2}{k}\,(t-3). \quad \text{.................... (17)}$$

Equation (17) has a root less than 5 if

$$4/k > 1 + e^{-2/k}, \quad \text{.......................... (18)}$$

which is an equality if $k = 2{\cdot}7$. Thus for $k = 1$ or 2 the maximum tension will occur before $t = 5$. If $k = 1$ the maximum tension is when $t = 3{\cdot}568$, and is equal to $3{\cdot}266\ gm/\varpi$, that is, 1·633 times the statical tension. If $k = 2$ the corresponding results are $t = 4{\cdot}368$, $2{\cdot}520\ gm/\varpi$, and 1·680 times the statical tension.

The third term enters at time 5, and afterwards is equal to

$$2\,[1 - e^{-(t-5)/k} - 2\,\{(t-5)/k\}^2\,e^{-(t-5)/k}].$$

If $k = 4$, the maximum stress is when $t = 6{\cdot}183$, and is equal to $2{\cdot}29\ gm/\varpi$. The statical tension is $1{\cdot}25\ gm/\varpi$, so that the ratio is 1·83.

Love proceeds by a method of continuation, but the present method is much more direct, and probably less troublesome in application.

4.6. To prove that the results given by the operational method, when applied to the vibrations of continuous systems, are actually correct, it is necessary to show that the solution actually satisfies the differential equation and that it gives the correct initial values of the displacement and the velocity at all points. The proof that it satisfies the initial conditions is difficult in the most general case, but Bromwich has gone far towards one. We have seen that in one of the simplest problems, that of the uniform string with the ends fixed, the verification that the solution is valid for the most general initial displacement is equivalent to Fourier's theorem. But for more specific problems the operational solution is equivalent to a single integral, and the direct verification that it satisfies the initial conditions is usually fairly easy. To show that it satisfies the differential equation, it would be natural to differentiate under the integral sign and substitute in the equation. But in practice it is usually found that the integrand, near the ends of the imaginary axis, is only small like some low power of $1/\lambda$ (the second in the problems of 4.3, 4.4, and 4.5), and consequently the integrals found by differentiating twice under the integral sign do not converge. But we can proceed as follows. If a part of our solution is

$$y = f(p)\, e^{px/c} = \frac{1}{2\pi\iota}\int_L f(\lambda) \exp \lambda \left(t + \frac{x}{c}\right) \frac{d\lambda}{\lambda}, \quad \text{.........(1)}$$

and this integral is intelligible for all values of x and t within a certain range, we have

$$\frac{\partial^2 y}{\partial t^2} = \operatorname*{Lim}_{h \to 0} \frac{y_{t+h} - 2y_t + y_{t-h}}{h^2}$$

$$= \operatorname*{Lim}_{h \to 0} \frac{1}{2\pi\iota}\int_L f(\lambda) \exp \lambda \left(t + \frac{x}{c}\right) \frac{e^{\lambda h} - 2 + e^{-\lambda h}}{h^2} \frac{d\lambda}{\lambda} \quad \text{....(2)}$$

Also
$$c^2 \frac{\partial^2 y}{\partial x^2} = c^2 \operatorname*{Lim}_{h \to 0} \frac{y_{x+ch} - 2y_x + y_{x-ch}}{c^2 h^2}$$

$$= \operatorname*{Lim}_{h \to 0} \frac{1}{2\pi\iota}\int_L f(\lambda) \exp \lambda \left(t + \frac{x}{c}\right) \frac{e^{\lambda h} - 2 + e^{-\lambda h}}{h^2} \frac{d\lambda}{\lambda}. \quad \text{...(3)}$$

The two integrals are identical before we proceed to the limit, and therefore their limiting values are the same. Hence

$$\frac{\partial^2 y}{\partial t^2} = c^2 \frac{\partial^2 y}{\partial x^2}, \quad \text{.........................(4)}$$

and the differential equation is satisfied. This argument does not assume that the derivatives of y are expressible as convergent integrals, but only that they exist.

The argument breaks down at points where the second derivatives do not exist; as for instance in 4.3 at the points where the slope of the curve formed by the string suddenly changes. At these points there is a discontinuity in the transverse component of the tension, so that the point has momentarily an infinite acceleration. This is why the velocity changes discontinuously when a wave arrives. The momentum of a given stretch of the string, however, varies continuously; the difficulty is the fault of the representation by a differential equation, not of the method of solution.

CHAPTER V

CONDUCTION OF HEAT IN ONE DIMENSION

5.1. The rate of transmission of heat across a surface by conduction is equal to $-k\partial V/\partial n$ per unit area, where V is the temperature, k a constant of the material called the thermal conductivity, and dn an element of the normal to the surface. Hence we can show easily that in a uniform solid the rate of flow of heat into an element of volume $dx\,dy\,dz$ is

$$k\nabla^2 V\,.\,dx\,dy\,dz.$$

But the quantity of heat required to produce a rise of temperature dV in unit mass is $c\,dV$, where c is the specific heat, and therefore that required to produce a rise dV in unit volume is $\rho c\,dV$, where ρ is the density. Hence the equation of heat conduction is

$$\frac{\partial}{\partial t}(\rho c V) = k\nabla^2 V. \qquad \text{(1)}$$

If we put

$$k/\rho c = h^2, \qquad \text{(2)}$$

h^2 is called the thermometric conductivity, and the equation becomes

$$\frac{\partial V}{\partial t} = h^2\nabla^2 V. \qquad \text{(3)}$$

In addition, there may be some other source of heat. If this would suffice to raise the temperature by P degrees per second if it stayed where it was generated, a term P must be added to the right of (3).

It is usually convenient to write p for $\partial/\partial t$, and

$$p = h^2 q^2. \qquad \text{(4)}$$

The operational solutions are then functions of q; but q must be expressed again in terms of p before interpreting.

5.2. Consider first a uniform rod, with its sides thermally insulated, and initially at temperature S. At time zero the end $x=0$ is cooled to temperature zero, and afterwards maintained at that temperature. The end $x=l$ is kept at temperature S. Find the variation of temperature at other points of the rod.

The problem being one-dimensional, the equation of heat conduction is

$$\frac{\partial V}{\partial t} - h^2\frac{\partial^2 V}{\partial x^2} = 0, \qquad \text{(1)}$$

while at time 0, V is equal to S. Hence the subsidiary equation is

$$pV - h^2 \frac{\partial^2 V}{\partial x^2} = pS, \qquad \text{(2)}$$

or

$$\frac{\partial^2 V}{\partial x^2} - q^2 V = -q^2 S. \qquad \text{(3)}$$

The end conditions are that

$$\left.\begin{array}{l} V = 0 \text{ when } x = 0, \\ V = S \text{ when } x = l. \end{array}\right\} \qquad \text{(4)}$$

Hence

$$V = S\left(1 - \frac{\sinh q(l-x)}{\sinh ql}\right). \qquad \text{(5)}$$

The integrand is an even function of q, and therefore a single-valued function of p. It has poles where

$$ql = \pm \iota n\pi; \text{ that is, } p = -h^2 n^2 \pi^2 / l^2, \qquad \text{(6)}$$

where n is any integer. But the negative values of q give the same values of p as the positive values, and therefore when we apply the partial-fraction rule we need consider only the positive values. The part arising from $p = 0$ is

$$S\left(1 - \frac{l-x}{l}\right) = S\frac{x}{l}. \qquad \text{(7)}$$

The general term is

$$-S \frac{\sinh \iota n\pi (l-x)/l}{(-h^2 n^2 \pi^2 / l^2) \cosh (\iota n\pi)\,(l^2/2h^2 \iota n\pi)} e^{-n^2\pi^2h^2t/l^2}$$

$$= S \frac{2}{n\pi} \sin \frac{n\pi x}{l} e^{-n^2\pi^2h^2t/l^2}, \qquad \text{(8)}$$

and the complete solution is

$$V = S\left[\frac{x}{l} + \sum_{n=1}^{\infty} \frac{2}{n\pi} \sin \frac{n\pi x}{l} e^{-n^2\pi^2h^2t/l^2}\right]. \qquad \text{(9)}$$

If $\pi h t^{\frac{1}{2}}/l$ is moderate, this series converges rapidly, and no more convenient solution could be desired. It evidently tends in the limit to the steady value Sx/l.

But if $\pi h t^{\frac{1}{2}}/l$ is small the convergence will be slow. In this case we may adopt a form of the expansion method applied to waves*. We can write (5) in the form

$$V = S\left[1 - e^{-qx}\left(1 - e^{-2q(l-x)}\right)\left(1 + e^{-2ql} + e^{-4ql} + \dots\right)\right]. \qquad \text{(10)}$$

For if we interpret this as an integral along the path L, the argument of q is between $\pm \frac{1}{4}\pi$ at all points of the path, and the series converges

* Heaviside, *Electromagnetic Theory*, 2, 69–79, 287–8.

uniformly. Integration term by term is therefore justifiable, and we may interpret term by term. Now

$$qx = xp^{\frac{1}{2}}/h, \quad \text{.............................(11)}$$

and by 2.4 (16)

$$e^{-qx} = 1 - \operatorname{erf} \frac{x}{2ht^{\frac{1}{2}}}. \quad \text{........................(12)}$$

Hence

$$V = S\left[\operatorname{erf} \frac{x}{2ht^{\frac{1}{2}}} + \left(1 - \operatorname{erf} \frac{2l - x}{2ht^{\frac{1}{2}}}\right) - \left(1 - \operatorname{erf} \frac{2l + x}{2ht^{\frac{1}{2}}}\right) - \dots\right] \text{....(13)}$$

When w is great, $1 - \operatorname{erf} w$ is small compared with e^{-w^2}. If then $x/2ht^{\frac{1}{2}}$ is moderate, but $l/2ht^{\frac{1}{2}}$ large, this series is rapidly convergent, and can in most cases be reduced to its first term. This solution is therefore convenient in those cases where (9) is not.

5.3. *One-dimensional flow of heat in a region infinite in both directions.* First suppose that at time 0 the distribution of temperature is given by

$$V = H(x). \quad \text{.............................(1)}$$

We have just seen that the function expressed in operational form by

$$e^{-qx} = 1 - \operatorname{erf} \frac{x}{2ht^{\frac{1}{2}}} \quad \text{...........................(2)}$$

satisfies the differential equation

$$\frac{\partial y}{\partial t} - h^2 \frac{\partial^2 y}{\partial x^2} = 0, \quad \text{..........................(3)}$$

for positive values of x; and by symmetry it will also satisfy it for negative values of x, since the function and its derivatives with regard to x are continuous when $x = 0$. Also when t tends to zero this function tends to zero for all positive values of x, and to 2 for all negative values. It follows from these facts that the function

$$\tfrac{1}{2}(2 - e^{-qx}) = \tfrac{1}{2}\left[1 + \operatorname{erf} \frac{x}{2ht^{\frac{1}{2}}}\right] \quad \text{..................(4)}$$

satisfies the differential equation for all values of x and all positive values of t; and when t tends to zero the function tends to zero for negative values of x, and to unity for positive values; that is, to $H(x)$. Hence this function is the solution required.

Suppose now that the initial distribution of temperature is

$$V = f(x), \quad \text{...............................(5)}$$

where $f(x)$ is any known function. Then this is equivalent to

$$V=\int_{\xi=-\infty}^{\infty} f(\xi)\, d\{H(\xi-x)\}. \quad \text{.................(6)}$$

But the solution for positive values of the time that reduces to $H(\xi-x)$ when $t=0$ is

$$\tfrac{1}{2}\left[1+\operatorname{erf}\frac{\xi-x}{2ht^{\frac{1}{2}}}\right].$$

Hence, by the principle of the superposibility of solutions, the solution of the more general problem is

$$V=\int_{\xi=-\infty}^{\infty} \tfrac{1}{2}f(\xi)\, d\left[1+\operatorname{erf}\frac{\xi-x}{2ht^{\frac{1}{2}}}\right] \quad \text{...............(7)}$$

$$=\frac{1}{\sqrt{\pi}}\int_{-\infty}^{\infty} f(\xi)\, e^{-(\xi-x)^2/4h^2t}\frac{d\xi}{2ht^{\frac{1}{2}}}. \quad \text{.................(8)}$$

Put now $$\xi=x+2ht^{\frac{1}{2}}\lambda. \quad \text{..........................(9)}$$

Then $$V=\frac{1}{\sqrt{\pi}}\int_{-\infty}^{\infty} f(x+2ht^{\frac{1}{2}}\lambda)\, e^{-\lambda^2}\, d\lambda. \quad \text{..............(10)}$$

This is the general solution obtained by Fourier.

5.4. If the temperature is kept constant at $x=0$, but the initial temperature is $f(x)$ for positive values of x, we may proceed as follows. If we consider instead a system infinite in both directions, but with the initial temperature specified for negative values of x so that

$$f(-x)=-f(x), \quad \text{..........................(1)}$$

we see that the temperature at $x=0$ will be zero at all later instants and the solution of this problem will fit the actual one. Hence

$$V=\frac{1}{\sqrt{\pi}}\int_0^{\infty} f(\xi)\, e^{-(\xi-x)^2/4h^2t}\frac{d\xi}{2ht^{\frac{1}{2}}}-\frac{1}{\sqrt{\pi}}\int_0^{\infty} f(\xi)\, e^{-(\xi+x)^2/4h^2t}\frac{d\xi}{2ht^{\frac{1}{2}}} \quad \text{......(2)}$$

$$=\frac{1}{\sqrt{\pi}}\int_{-x/2ht^{\frac{1}{2}}}^{\infty} f(x+2ht^{\frac{1}{2}}\lambda)\, e^{-\lambda^2}d\lambda-\frac{1}{\sqrt{\pi}}\int_{x/2ht^{\frac{1}{2}}}^{\infty} f(-x+2ht^{\frac{1}{2}}\lambda)\, e^{-\lambda^2}d\lambda \quad \text{.........(3)}$$

If in particular the initial temperature is everywhere S, $f(\xi)=S$, and

$$V=S.\frac{1}{\sqrt{\pi}}\int_{-x/2ht^{\frac{1}{2}}}^{x/2ht^{\frac{1}{2}}} e^{-\lambda^2}\, d\lambda$$

$$=S\operatorname{erf}\frac{x}{2ht^{\frac{1}{2}}}. \quad \text{..................................(4)}$$

Thus the solution of 5.2 is regenerated. In Kelvin's solution of the problem of the cooling of the earth, 5.3 (10) was adapted to a semi-infinite region in this way.

The value of $\partial V/\partial x$ at the end $x=0$ is obtainable by differentiating the solution valid for a semi-infinite region. In Kelvin's problem

$$V = S(1 - e^{-qx}),$$

and

$$\left(\frac{\partial V}{\partial x}\right)_{x=0} = Sq = \frac{S}{h(\pi t)^{\frac{1}{2}}}. \qquad \text{.........................(5)}$$

The same result is found by differentiating (4).

We notice the curious fact that although the original exact solution for a finite region in 5.2 (5) is a single-valued function of p, a square root of t appears in the approximate solution for a greatly extended region. The reason can be seen by differentiating the exact solution. It gives

$$\left(\frac{\partial V}{\partial x}\right)_{x=0} = Sq \coth ql, \qquad \text{......................(6)}$$

which is a single-valued function of p. But when we use Bromwich's interpretation we find that

$$\left(\frac{\partial V}{\partial x}\right)_{x=0} = \frac{1}{2\pi\iota} S \int_L \frac{\lambda^{-\frac{1}{2}}}{h} \coth\left(\frac{\lambda^{\frac{1}{2}} l}{h}\right) e^{\lambda t}\, d\lambda, \qquad \text{...........(7)}$$

which is again single valued; but if $\lambda^{\frac{1}{2}}$ is specified to be real and positive when λ is real and positive, it has a positive real part at all points on L, and therefore if l is great $\coth \lambda^{\frac{1}{2}} l/h$ is practically unity. The integral is therefore equivalent to

$$\frac{1}{2\pi\iota} S \int_L \frac{\lambda^{-\frac{1}{2}}}{h} e^{\lambda t}\, d\lambda, \qquad \text{.........................(8)}$$

which is our interpretation of $p^{\frac{1}{2}} S/h$, and is equal to $S/h\sqrt{(\pi t)}$. We could have started by specifying the sign of $\lambda^{\frac{1}{2}}$ to be negative when λ is positive, but then $\lambda^{\frac{1}{2}}$ and $\coth \lambda^{\frac{1}{2}} l/h$ would both have been simply reversed in sign, and the same answer would have been obtained.

5.5. *Imperfect cooling at the free end of a one-dimensional region.* With the initial conditions of 5.2, let us suppose that the end $x=l$ is maintained at temperature S as before, but that the end $x=0$ is not effectively cooled to temperature zero. Instead we suppose that it radiates away heat at a rate proportional to its temperature. At the same time heat is conducted to the end at a rate $k\partial V/\partial x$ per unit area. These effects must balance if the temperature at the surface is to vary continuously, so that instead of having $V=0$ at the end as before we shall have a relation of the form

$$\frac{\partial V}{\partial x} - \alpha V = 0 \text{ at } x = 0. \quad \text{.........................(1)}$$

The equation 5.2 (3) is unaltered, and the operational solution is

$$V = S\{1 - A \sinh q(l-x)\}, \quad \text{....................(2)}$$

where A is to be determined to satisfy (1). Hence

$$qA \cosh ql - \alpha(1 - A \sinh ql) = 0 \quad \text{..................(3)}$$

and

$$V = S\left\{1 - \frac{\alpha \sinh q(l-x)}{q \cosh ql + \alpha \sinh ql}\right\}. \quad \text{..................(4)}$$

The roots in p are real and negative, and we can proceed to an interpretation by the partial-fraction rule as usual. Or, using the expansion in 'waves,' we have

$$V = S\left[1 - \frac{\alpha e^{-qx}}{q+\alpha}\left(1 - e^{-2q(l-x)}\right)\left(1 - \frac{q-\alpha}{q+\alpha} e^{-2ql} + \dots\right)\right]. \quad \text{...(5)}$$

If the length is great enough to make the terms involving e^{-2ql} inappreciable, we can reduce this to its first two terms, thus:

$$V = S\left[1 - \frac{\alpha e^{-qx}}{q+\alpha}\right] \quad \text{..........................(6)}$$

If α is great, the solutions reduce to those of 5.2; this is to be expected, for (1) then implies that $V=0$ when $x=0$, which is the boundary condition adopted in 5.2. If α is small, V reduces to S; the reason is that this implies that there is no loss of heat from the end, and therefore the temperature does not change anywhere. For intermediate values we may proceed as follows. If

$$y = \frac{\alpha e^{-qx}}{q+\alpha}, \quad \text{.................................(7)}$$

Bromwich's rule gives

$$y = \frac{1}{2\pi\iota}\int_L \frac{\alpha h}{\lambda^{\frac{1}{2}} + \alpha h} \exp\left(\lambda t - \frac{\lambda^{\frac{1}{2}} x}{h}\right)\frac{d\lambda}{\lambda}. \quad \text{...............(8)}$$

Put

$$\lambda = \kappa^2. \quad \text{..................................(9)}$$

The path of integration for κ is a curve going from $Re^{-\frac{1}{4}\pi\iota}$ to $Re^{\frac{1}{4}\pi\iota}$, where R is great, passing on the way within a finite distance of the origin on the positive side. Denote this path by M. Then

$$y = \frac{1}{\pi\iota}\int_M \frac{\alpha h}{(\kappa + \alpha h)\kappa} \exp\left(\kappa^2 t - \frac{\kappa x}{h}\right) d\kappa \quad \text{...............(10)}$$

$$= \frac{1}{\pi\iota}\int_M \left(\frac{1}{\kappa} - \frac{1}{\kappa + \alpha h}\right) \exp\left(\kappa^2 t - \frac{\kappa x}{h}\right) d\kappa. \quad \text{.........(11)}$$

But
$$\frac{1}{\pi\iota}\int_M \frac{1}{\kappa}\exp\left(\kappa^2 t-\frac{\kappa x}{h}\right)d\kappa=\frac{1}{2\pi\iota}\int_L \exp\left(\lambda t-\frac{\lambda^{\frac{1}{2}}x}{h}\right)\frac{d\lambda}{\lambda}$$
$$=e^{-qx}$$
$$=1-\operatorname{erf}\frac{x}{2ht^{\frac{1}{2}}}. \qquad\text{.............}(12)$$

The second part of (11) can be written as an integral with regard to μ, where
$$\mu=\kappa+ah \qquad\text{..........................}(13)$$
along a path obtained by displacing M through a distance ah; but the integrand is regular between these paths and the route M may still be used. The second part is therefore
$$-\frac{1}{\pi\iota}\int_M \frac{1}{\mu}\exp\left\{\mu^2 t-\mu\left(2aht+\frac{x}{h}\right)\right\}\exp\left(a^2h^2t+ax\right)d\mu$$
$$=-\exp\left(a^2h^2t+ax\right)\left\{1-\operatorname{erf}\frac{x+2ah^2t}{2ht^{\frac{1}{2}}}\right\} \qquad\text{.............}(14)$$
and
$$y=1-\operatorname{erf}\xi-\exp\left(\gamma^2+ax\right)\{1-\operatorname{erf}(\xi+\gamma)\}, \qquad\text{......}(15)$$
where
$$\xi=x/2ht^{\frac{1}{2}};\ \gamma=aht^{\frac{1}{2}}. \qquad\text{.......................}(16)$$
Hence
$$V=S[\operatorname{erf}\xi+\exp(\gamma^2+ax)\{1-\operatorname{erf}(\xi+\gamma)\}]. \qquad\text{......}(17)$$
This is the same as Riemann's solution*.

The temperature at the end is
$$V_{x=0}=S\exp\gamma^2\{1-\operatorname{erf}\gamma\}, \qquad\text{.................}(18)$$
whence the temperature gradient at the end follows by (1). For small values of the time the temperature at the free end falls continuously; the temperature gradient there is not instantaneously infinite as in 5.4 (5). For great values of the time we can use the approximation 2.4 (28), giving
$$V_{x=0}=\frac{S}{ah\sqrt{(\pi t)}}\left[1-\frac{1}{2}\left(\frac{1}{a^2h^2t}\right)+\frac{1}{2}\cdot\frac{3}{2}\cdot\left(\frac{1}{a^2h^2t}\right)^2+\dots\right]. \qquad (19)$$

This is equivalent to one found by Heaviside†. Heaviside gives also an expansion in a convergent series, suitable for small values of t, but it is probably less convenient than the equivalent expression (18) in finite terms. We see from (19) that the longer the time taken the better is the approximation to $(\partial V/\partial x)_{x=0}$ given by the simple theory of 5.2.

* Riemann-Weber, *Partielle Differentialgleichungen*, 2, 1912, 95–98.

† *Electromagnetic Theory*, 2, 15.

5.6. A long rod is fastened at the end $x=0$, the other end not being in contact with a conductor. Initially it is at temperature 0, but at time 0 the clamped end is raised to temperature S and kept there. Each part of the rod loses heat by radiation at a rate proportional to its temperature. The differential equation is now

$$\frac{\partial V}{\partial t}=h^2\frac{\partial^2 V}{\partial x^2}-a^2 V, \qquad \text{.........................(1)}$$

where a is a constant. Let us put

$$p+a^2=h^2r^2 \qquad \text{..............................(2)}$$

and write the equation

$$\frac{\partial^2 V}{\partial x^2}-r^2V=0. \qquad \text{...........................(3)}$$

At $x=l$ there is no conduction out of the rod, and therefore $\partial V/\partial x$ vanishes. Also $V=S$ when $x=0$. The solution is

$$V=S\,\frac{\cosh r(l-x)}{\cosh rl}. \qquad \text{.........................(4)}$$

This can be expanded in powers of e^{-2rl}. The first term, which is the only one we require, is

$$V=Se^{-rx} \qquad \text{...(5)}$$

$$=\frac{S}{2\pi\iota}\int_L \exp\left\{\lambda t-\frac{(\lambda+a^2)^{\frac{1}{2}}x}{h}\right\}\frac{d\lambda}{\lambda}. \qquad \text{...............(6)}$$

Put

$$\lambda+a^2=\kappa^2. \qquad \text{..............................(7)}$$

Then

$$V=\frac{S}{\pi\iota}\int_M \exp\left\{(\kappa^2-a^2)t-\frac{\kappa x}{h}\right\}\frac{\kappa\,d\kappa}{\kappa^2-a^2}$$

$$=\frac{S}{2\pi\iota}\int_M \exp\left\{(\kappa^2-a^2)t-\frac{\kappa x}{h}\right\}\left\{\frac{1}{\kappa-a}+\frac{1}{\kappa+a}\right\}d\kappa. \qquad \text{...(8)}$$

But if

$$\kappa=a+\mu \qquad \text{..............................(9)}$$

the term in $1/(\kappa-a)$ becomes

$$\frac{S}{2\pi\iota}\int_M \exp\left\{\mu^2 t-\mu\left(\frac{x}{h}-2at\right)\right\}\exp\left(-\frac{ax}{h}\right)\frac{d\mu}{\mu}$$

$$=\tfrac{1}{2}S\exp\left(-\frac{ax}{h}\right)\left\{1-\operatorname{erf}\frac{x-2aht}{2ht^{\frac{1}{2}}}\right\} \qquad \text{...........(10)}$$

as in 5.5 (14). The complete solution is

$$V=\tfrac{1}{2}S\left[\exp\left(-\frac{ax}{h}\right)\left\{1-\operatorname{erf}\frac{x-2aht}{2ht^{\frac{1}{2}}}\right\}\right.$$

$$\left.+\exp\left(\frac{ax}{h}\right)\left\{1-\operatorname{erf}\frac{x+2aht}{2ht^{\frac{1}{2}}}\right\}\right]. \qquad \text{...(11)}$$

When $a=0$ this reduces to

$$V=S\left(1-\operatorname{erf}\frac{x}{2ht^{\frac{1}{2}}}\right), \qquad \text{.....................(12)}$$

so that the disturbance of temperature spreads along the rod, the time needed to produce a given rise of temperature at distance x from the end being proportional to x^2. If t is small enough to make $at^{\frac{1}{2}}$ small, the error functions will be practically unity except where x is not great compared with $2ht^{\frac{1}{2}}$. For such values of x the exponentials are nearly unity. Thus at first the heating proceeds almost as in the absence of radiation from the sides of the rod.

But if $at^{\frac{1}{2}}$ is great and $x/2ht^{\frac{1}{2}}$ small or moderate, the first error function in (11) is practically -1, and the second $+1$. Thus in these conditions

$$V=Se^{-ax/h}. \qquad \text{..........................(13)}$$

This is seen by a return to the original equation to be the solution corresponding to a steady state. This will hold so long as $at^{\frac{1}{2}}-x/2ht^{\frac{1}{2}}$ is large and positive, even if $x/2ht^{\frac{1}{2}}$ is itself large. The region where the approximation (13) is valid therefore spreads along the rod with velocity $2ah$; if $at^{\frac{1}{2}}$ has once become large, each point on the rod reaches a nearly steady temperature at a time rather greater than $x/2ah$.

If $at^{\frac{1}{2}}$ is large and $x/2ht^{\frac{1}{2}}$ still greater, the solution is nearly

$$V=\tfrac{1}{2}Se^{-ax/h}\left\{1+\operatorname{erf}\frac{x-2aht}{2ht^{\frac{1}{2}}}\right\}. \qquad \text{...............(14)}$$

If further the argument of the error function is large, we can write

$$V=\frac{1}{2\sqrt{\pi}}Se^{-ax/h}\exp\left\{-\frac{(x-2aht)^2}{4h^2t}\right\}\frac{2ht^{\frac{1}{2}}}{x-2aht}$$

$$=\frac{1}{\sqrt{\pi}}S\exp\left\{-\frac{x^2}{4h^2t}-a^2t\right\}\frac{ht^{\frac{1}{2}}}{x-2aht}. \qquad \text{...............(15)}$$

In the regions that have not reached their steady state, the temperature resembles that for the problem without radiation, except that the small factor $\frac{1}{2}e^{-a^2t}\dfrac{x}{x-2aht}$ must be introduced.

5.7. *The cooling of the earth.* Cooling in the earth since it first became solid has probably not had time to become appreciable except within a layer whose thickness is small compared with the radius. It is therefore legitimate to neglect the effects of curvature and treat the problem as one-dimensional. Radiation from the outer surface must have soon reduced the temperature there to that maintained by solar radiation, so that we may suppose the surface temperature to be constant and adopt it for our zero of temperature. The chief difference from the problem of 5.2 is that we must allow for the heating effect of radioactivity in the outer layers. Suppose first that the quantity P defined in 5.1 is equal to a constant A down to a depth H, and zero below that depth. Take the initial temperature to be $S+mx$, where m is a constant. Then the subsidiary equation is

$$\left.\begin{aligned} \frac{\partial^2 V}{\partial x^2} - q^2 V &= -\frac{A}{h^2} - q^2(S+mx) \qquad 0<x<H \\ \text{and} \qquad &= -q^2(S+mx) \qquad H<x, \end{aligned}\right\}\quad\ldots\ldots\ldots(1)$$

and the solutions are

$$\left.\begin{aligned} V &= \frac{A}{q^2 h^2} + S + mx + Be^{-qx} + Ce^{qx} \qquad 0<x<H \\ \text{and} \qquad &= S + mx + De^{-qx} \qquad H<x. \end{aligned}\right\}\quad\ldots\ldots\ldots(2)$$

A term in e^{qx} is not required in the solution for great depths, because it would imply that the temperature there suddenly dropped a finite amount at all depths, however great, in consequence of a disturbance near the surface. The conditions to determine B, C, and D are that V vanishes at $x=0$, and that V and $\partial V/\partial x$ are continuous at $x=H$. Hence

$$B + C + S + A/p = 0, \quad\ldots\ldots\ldots(3)$$

$$Be^{-qH} + Ce^{qH} + A/p = De^{-qH}, \quad\ldots\ldots\ldots(4)$$

$$Be^{-qH} - Ce^{qH} = De^{-qH}. \quad\ldots\ldots\ldots(5)$$

Solving and substituting in (2), we find

$$\left.\begin{aligned} V &= S(1-e^{-qx}) + mx + \frac{A}{p}\{1 - e^{-qx} - e^{-qH}\sinh qx\} \qquad 0<x<H \\ V &= S(1-e^{-qx}) + mx + \frac{A}{p}(\cosh qH - 1)\, e^{-qx} \qquad x>H. \end{aligned}\right\}\quad(6)$$

These solutions involve terms of the form $\frac{1}{p}e^{-qa}$, where a is positive. To interpret, we write

$$\begin{aligned} \frac{1}{p}e^{-qa} &= \frac{1}{2\pi\iota}\int_L \exp\left(\lambda t - \frac{\lambda^{\frac{1}{2}} a}{h}\right)\frac{d\lambda}{\lambda^2} \\ &= \frac{1}{\pi\iota}\int_M \exp\left(\kappa^2 t - \frac{\kappa a}{h}\right)\frac{d\kappa}{\kappa^3} \\ &= \frac{1}{2\pi\iota}\int_M \left(\frac{2t}{\kappa} - \frac{a}{h\kappa^2}\right)\exp\left(\kappa^2 t - \frac{\kappa a}{h}\right) d\kappa \quad\ldots\ldots\ldots(7) \end{aligned}$$

on integrating by parts. But

$$\frac{1}{\pi\iota}\int_M \exp\left(\kappa^2 t - \frac{\kappa a}{h}\right)\frac{d\kappa}{\kappa} = e^{-qa} \quad \text{..................(8)}$$

and a further integration by parts gives

$$\frac{1}{2\pi\iota}\int_M \exp\left(\kappa^2 t - \frac{\kappa a}{h}\right)\frac{d\kappa}{\kappa^2} = \frac{1}{2\pi\iota}\int_M \left(2t - \frac{a}{h\kappa}\right)\exp\left(\kappa^2 t - \frac{\kappa a}{h}\right)d\kappa$$

$$= htqe^{-qa} - \frac{a}{2h}e^{-qa}. \quad \text{...(9)}$$

In all $$\frac{1}{p}e^{-qa} = \left(t + \frac{a^2}{2h^2}\right)\left(1 - \operatorname{erf}\frac{a}{2ht^{\frac{1}{2}}}\right) - \frac{a}{h}\sqrt{\frac{t}{\pi}}\,e^{-a^2/4h^2 t}. \quad \text{...(10)}$$

Thus we can obtain a solution in finite terms, which is easily seen to be identical with that previously obtained by a more laborious method *.

The temperature gradient at the surface is found most easily from (6); we have

$$\left(\frac{\partial V}{\partial x}\right)_{x=0} = Sq + m + \frac{A}{p}\left(q - qe^{-qH}\right). \quad \text{...............(11)}$$

But $$\frac{1}{q}e^{-qH} = \frac{h}{2\pi\iota}\int_L \exp\left(\lambda t - \frac{\lambda^{\frac{1}{2}}H}{h}\right)\frac{d\lambda}{\lambda^{\frac{3}{2}}} \quad \text{....................(12)}$$

$$= \frac{h}{\pi\iota}\int_M \exp\left(\kappa^2 t - \frac{\kappa H}{h}\right)\frac{d\kappa}{\kappa^2}$$

$$= 2h^2 tqe^{-qH} - He^{-qH}$$

$$= 2h\,(t/\pi)^{\frac{1}{2}}\,e^{-H^2/4h^2 t} - H\left(1 - \operatorname{erf}\frac{H}{2ht^{\frac{1}{2}}}\right) \quad \text{......(13)}$$

and therefore

$$\left(\frac{\partial V}{\partial x}\right)_{x=0} = \frac{S}{h(\pi t)^{\frac{1}{2}}} + m + \frac{A}{h^2}\left[H - H\operatorname{erf}\frac{H}{2ht^{\frac{1}{2}}} + 2h\left(\frac{t}{\pi}\right)^{\frac{1}{2}}\left(1 - e^{-H^2/4h^2 t}\right)\right]. \quad \text{.........(14)}$$

This is identical with the result given in earlier works of mine except that in these the factor 2 was omitted from the last term, which is small.

In the actual problem a considerable simplification arises from the fact that H is small compared with $2ht^{\frac{1}{2}}$. On this account we can expand the solutions in powers of H, and retain only the earlier terms. Thus for the surface temperature gradient we have

$$\left(\frac{\partial V}{\partial x}\right)_{x=0} = Sq + m + \frac{A}{h^2 q^2}\cdot q\cdot\left(qH - \tfrac{1}{2}q^2H^2\right)$$

$$= \frac{S}{h(\pi t)^{\frac{1}{2}}} + m + \frac{AH}{h^2}\left(1 - \frac{H}{2h(\pi t)^{\frac{1}{2}}}\right) \quad \text{.........(15)}$$

* Jeffreys, *Phil. Mag.* 32, 1916, 575–591; *The Earth*, 1924, 84.

and for the temperature at depths greater than H

$$V = S(1 - e^{-qx}) + mx + \frac{A}{h^2 q^2} \cdot \tfrac{1}{2} q^2 H^2 \,.\, e^{-qx}$$

$$= mx + \left(S - \frac{AH^2}{2h^2}\right) \operatorname{erf} \frac{x}{2ht^{\frac{1}{2}}} + \frac{AH^2}{2h^2} \,. \quad \text{............(16)}$$

5.71. An alternative possibility is that the radioactive generation of heat, instead of being confined entirely to a uniform surface layer, may decrease exponentially with depth. In this case the subsidiary equation is

$$\frac{\partial^2 V}{\partial x^2} - q^2 V = -\frac{A}{h^2} e^{-ax} - q^2 (S + mx) \quad \text{...............(1)}$$

at all depths. We already know the part of the solution contributed by $S + mx$. The remainder is

$$W = \frac{A}{h^2} \frac{e^{-ax} - e^{-qx}}{q^2 - a^2} \,. \quad \text{........................(2)}$$

But

$$\frac{e^{-ax}}{h^2 (q^2 - a^2)} = \frac{e^{-ax}}{p - h^2 a^2} = \frac{1}{h^2 a^2} e^{-ax} (e^{h^2 a^2 t} - 1) \quad \text{............(3)}$$

and

$$-\frac{a^2 e^{-qx}}{q^2 - a^2} = \tfrac{1}{2} \left(\frac{a}{q + a} - \frac{a}{q - a}\right) e^{-qx}$$

$$= \tfrac{1}{2} [e^{-qx} - \exp(\gamma^2 + ax) \{1 - \operatorname{erf}(\xi + \gamma)\}]$$

$$+ \tfrac{1}{2} [e^{-qx} - \exp(\gamma^2 - ax) \{1 - \operatorname{erf}(\xi - \gamma)\}], \quad \text{.........(4)}$$

where

$$\xi = x/2ht^{\frac{1}{2}}\,; \quad \gamma = aht^{\frac{1}{2}}. \quad \text{.......................(5)}$$

Hence

$$W = \frac{A}{h^2 a^2} \{\exp(\gamma^2 - ax) - \exp(-ax)\}$$

$$+ \frac{A}{h^2 a^2} [(1 - \operatorname{erf} \xi) - \tfrac{1}{2} \exp(\gamma^2 + ax) \{1 - \operatorname{erf}(\xi + \gamma)\}$$

$$- \tfrac{1}{2} \exp(\gamma^2 - ax) \{1 - \operatorname{erf}(\xi - \gamma)\}]$$

$$= \frac{A}{h^2 a^2} [1 - \operatorname{erf} \xi - e^{-ax} - \tfrac{1}{2} \exp(\gamma^2 + ax) \{1 - \operatorname{erf}(\xi + \gamma)\}$$

$$+ \tfrac{1}{2} \exp(\gamma^2 - ax) \{1 + \operatorname{erf}(\gamma - \xi)\}], \quad \text{...(6)}$$

which is the same as the solution obtained by Ingersoll and Zobel*.

The contribution of radioactivity to the temperature gradient at the surface is

$$\left(\frac{\partial W}{\partial x}\right)_{x=0} = \frac{A}{h^2} \frac{1}{q + a} \quad \text{..................................(7)}$$

$$= \frac{A}{h^2 a} \{1 - \exp \gamma^2 (1 - \operatorname{erf} \gamma)\}. \quad \text{............(8)}$$

* *Mathematical Theory of Heat Conduction*, Ginn, 1913.

When γ is great, as it actually is, we have

$$\left(\frac{\partial W}{\partial x}\right)_{x=0}=\frac{A}{h^2 a}\left(1-\frac{1}{\gamma\sqrt{\pi}}\right)=\frac{A}{h^2 a}\left(1-\frac{1}{ah\sqrt{(\pi t)}}\right). \quad \text{......(9)}$$

5.8. The justification of the method is easier in problems of heat conduction than in those of the last chapter, because the integrands always contain a factor $\exp\left(-\frac{\lambda^{\frac{1}{2}}x}{h}\right)$. This tends to zero when λ tends to $c\pm\iota\infty$ in such a way that the integrals obtained by differentiating under the integral sign always converge, and can therefore be substituted in the differential equation directly. But the integrals for the temperature are of the form

$$V=\frac{1}{2\pi\iota}\int f(\lambda)\exp\left(\lambda t-\frac{\lambda^{\frac{1}{2}}x}{h}\right)\frac{d\lambda}{\lambda}$$

and when we substitute in the equation

$$\frac{\partial V}{\partial t}-h^2\frac{\partial^2 V}{\partial x^2}=0$$

the integrand vanishes identically.

CHAPTER VI

PROBLEMS WITH SPHERICAL OR CYLINDRICAL SYMMETRY

6.1. So far we have treated only problems of wave transmission or conduction of heat in one dimension. If our system has spherical symmetry, the equation of transmission of sound takes the form

$$\frac{\partial^2\Phi}{\partial t^2}-c^2\nabla^2\Phi=0, \quad \text{......(1)}$$

where Φ is the velocity potential, and

$$\nabla^2\Phi=\frac{1}{r^2}\frac{\partial}{\partial r}\left(r^2\frac{\partial\Phi}{\partial r}\right)=\frac{\partial^2\Phi}{\partial r^2}+\frac{2}{r}\frac{\partial\Phi}{\partial r}$$

$$=\frac{1}{r}\frac{\partial^2}{\partial r^2}(r\Phi). \quad \text{......(2)}$$

The differential equation is therefore equivalent to

$$\frac{\partial^2}{c^2 \partial t^2}(r\Phi) - \frac{\partial^2}{\partial r^2}(r\Phi) = 0. \quad \text{.....................(3)}$$

This is of the same form as the equation of transmission of sound in one dimension, $r\Phi$ taking the place of Φ; but differences of treatment arise from differences in the boundary conditions. A similar transformation can of course be applied to the equation of heat conduction.

If the symmetry is cylindrical, we take Cartesian coordinates x, y, z, and put

$$x^2 + y^2 = \varpi^2, \quad y = x \tan \phi, \quad \text{.....................(4)}$$

and if Φ is independent of z and ϕ we have

$$\nabla^2 \Phi = \frac{1}{\varpi} \frac{\partial}{\partial \varpi}\left(\varpi \frac{\partial \Phi}{\partial \varpi}\right), \quad \text{.....................(5)}$$

which is capable of no simple transformation analogous to that just given for the case of spherical symmetry. This fact is connected with striking differences between the phenomena of wave motion in two and and three dimensions.

6.2. Consider first a spherical region of high pressure, surrounded by an infinitely extended region of uniform pressure; the boundary between them is solid, and the whole is at rest. Suddenly the boundary is annihilated. Find the subsequent motion. The problem is that of an explosion wave. We suppose the motion small enough to permit the neglect of squares of the displacements. At all points

$$\left(\frac{\partial^2}{\partial t^2} - c^2 \frac{\partial^2}{\partial r^2}\right) r\Phi = 0. \quad \text{.....................(1)}$$

Initially there is no motion, so that Φ is constant, and may be taken as zero. The excess pressure P is $-\rho \partial\Phi/\partial t$, where ρ is the density; this is initially a positive constant P_0 when $r < a$, but zero when $r > a$. Then we can take the subsidiary equations to be

$$\left.\begin{aligned} \left(\frac{\partial^2}{\partial r^2} - \frac{p^2}{c^2}\right)(r\Phi) &= \frac{P_0}{\rho c^2} pr \qquad r < a \\ &= 0 \qquad\qquad r > a. \end{aligned}\right\} \quad \text{.....................(2)}$$

The pressure must remain finite at the centre. Hence

$$r\Phi = -\frac{P_0 r}{\rho p} + A \sinh \frac{pr}{c} \qquad r < a \quad \text{..............(3)}$$

$$= B \exp(-pr/c) \qquad r > a. \quad \text{..............(4)}$$

There can be no term in $\exp(pr/c)$ in (4) since it would correspond to a wave travelling inwards. Now the pressure and the radial velocity must be continuous at $r=a$; hence Φ and $\partial\Phi/\partial r$ must be continuous. These give

$$-\frac{P_0 a}{\rho p}+A\sinh\frac{pa}{c}=B\exp\left(-\frac{pa}{c}\right), \quad \text{.................(5)}$$

$$-\frac{P_0}{\rho p}+\frac{p}{c}A\cosh\frac{pa}{c}=-\frac{p}{c}B\exp\left(-\frac{pa}{c}\right), \quad \text{...........(6)}$$

whence

$$A=\frac{P_0}{\rho p^2}(c+ap)\,e^{-pa/c};\ B=\frac{P_0}{2\rho p^2}(c-ap)\,e^{pa/c}-\frac{P_0}{2\rho p^2}(c+ap)\,e^{-pa/c}. \quad \text{......(7)}$$

Thus outside the original sphere

$$\frac{\rho}{P_0}r\Phi=\frac{1}{2p^2}(c-ap)\,e^{-p(r-a)/c}-\frac{1}{2p^2}(c+ap)\,e^{-p(r+a)/c}\text{....(8)}$$

The associated pressure change is

$$P=-\frac{P_0}{2r}\left[\left(\frac{c}{p}-a\right)e^{-p(r-a)/c}-\left(\frac{c}{p}+a\right)e^{-p(r+a)/c}\right]. \quad \text{...(9)}$$

But

$$\left.\begin{aligned}\frac{c}{p}-a&=0\text{ when }t\text{ is negative}\\&=ct-a\text{ when }t\text{ is positive.}\end{aligned}\right\} \quad \text{..............(10)}$$

Hence

$$\left(\frac{c}{p}-a\right)e^{-p(r-a)/c}=0\text{ when }ct<r-a$$

and

$$\begin{aligned}&=ct-(r-a)-a\\&=ct-r\text{ when }ct>r-a. \quad \text{......(11)}\end{aligned}$$

Similarly

$$\left(\frac{c}{p}+a\right)e^{-p(r+a)/c}=0\text{ when }ct<r+a$$

and

$$=ct-r\text{ when }ct>r+a. \quad \text{......(12)}$$

Hence the pressure disturbance is zero up to time $(r-a)/c$, when the first wave from the compressed region arrives, and after $(r+a)/c$, when the last wave passes. At intermediate times it is equal to $\frac{P_0}{2r}(r-ct)$. Thus it is equal to $P_0 a/2r$ when the first wave comes, $-P_0 a/2r$ when the last leaves, and varies linearly with the time in between. The compression in front of the shock is associated with an equal rarefaction in the rear*.

Within the sphere the pressure is

$$\frac{P_0 p}{r}\left[\frac{r}{p}-\frac{1}{p^2}(c+ap)\sinh\frac{pr}{c}\,e^{-pa/c}\right]$$

$$=\rho\left[1-\frac{1}{2r}\left(\frac{c}{p}+a\right)\left(e^{-p(a-r)/c}-e^{-p(a+r)/c}\right)\right]. \quad \text{...(13)}$$

* Cf. Stokes, *Phil. Mag.* 34, 1849, 52.

This is equal to P_0 up to time $(a-r)/c$, then drops suddenly to $P_0(1-a/2r)$, decreases linearly with the time till it reaches $-P_0 a/2r$ at time $(a+r)/c$, and then rises suddenly to zero. The infinity in the pressure at the centre is only instantaneous, for the time the disturbance lasts at a given place is $2r/c$, which vanishes at the centre. It is due to the simultaneous arrival of the waves from all points on the surface of the sphere; at other points the waves from different parts of the surface arrive at different times, giving a finite disturbance of pressure over a finite interval. If $r < \frac{1}{2}a$, the pressure becomes negative immediately on the arrival of the disturbance.

The behaviour of the velocity at distant points is similar to that of the pressure. If u is the radial velocity,

$$\begin{aligned} u &= \partial\Phi/\partial r \\ &= -p\Phi/c - \Phi/r. \qquad \text{.....................(14)} \end{aligned}$$

If r is great the first term is proportional to $1/r$, the second to $1/r^2$. The first is therefore the more important. But the first term is simply a multiple of the pressure. Hence it gives no motion at a point until time $(r-a)/c$, when the matter suddenly begins to move out with velocity $P_0 a/2\rho cr$. This velocity decreases linearly until time $(r+a)/c$, when it is $-P_0 a/2\rho cr$, and then suddenly ceases. The total outward displacement contributed is zero. The second term, however, gives a small velocity which vanishes at the beginning and end of the shock, and reaches a positive maximum at time r/c. It produces a residual displacement, of order a/r times the greatest given by the first term; this represents the fact that the matter originally compressed expands till it reaches normal pressure, and the surrounding matter moves outwards to make room for it.

6.21. Consider next the analogous problem with cylindrical symmetry. With analogous initial conditions, the subsidiary equation is

$$\left.\begin{aligned} \frac{1}{\varpi}\frac{\partial}{\partial\varpi}\left(\varpi\frac{\partial\Phi}{\partial\varpi}\right) - \frac{p^2}{c^2}\Phi &= \frac{P_0 p}{\rho c^2} \quad \varpi < a \\ &= 0 \qquad \varpi > a. \end{aligned}\right\} \qquad \text{..............(1)}$$

The solutions are Bessel functions of imaginary argument and order zero, $I_0(p\varpi/c)$ and $K_0(p\varpi/c)$. The latter is inadmissible within the cylinder, because it is infinite when $\varpi = 0$. The former cannot occur outside it, for the following reason. The interpretation is to be an integral along a route through values of the variable with positive real parts, and when ϖ is great the asymptotic expansion of $I_0(\lambda\varpi/c)$ contains $\exp(\lambda\varpi/c)$ as a factor. Hence the solution would involve $\exp(p\varpi/c)$

and therefore a disturbance travelling inwards. The solutions are therefore

$$\left.\begin{aligned}\Phi &= -\frac{P_0}{\rho p} + A I_0\left(\frac{p\varpi}{c}\right) \qquad 0 < \varpi < a \\ &= B K_0\left(\frac{p\varpi}{c}\right) \qquad a < \varpi.\end{aligned}\right\} \qquad \text{.................(2)}$$

Also $\partial\Phi/\partial t$ and $\partial\Phi/\partial\varpi$ must be continuous at $\varpi = a$. Hence

$$A I_0\left(\frac{pa}{c}\right) - \frac{P_0}{\rho p} = B K_0\left(\frac{pa}{c}\right), \qquad \text{..............(3)}$$

$$A I_0'\left(\frac{pa}{c}\right) \qquad = B K_0'\left(\frac{pa}{c}\right). \qquad \text{...............(4)}$$

Also, with the definitions below, we have the identity

$$I_0'(z)\, K_0(z) - I_0(z)\, K_0'(z) = 2/\pi z. \qquad \text{..............(5)}$$

Hence we find for points outside $\varpi = a$,

$$\begin{aligned}\frac{\rho\Phi}{P_0} &= -\frac{\pi}{2}\frac{a}{c} I_0'\left(\frac{pa}{c}\right) K_0\left(\frac{p\varpi}{c}\right) \\ &= -\frac{1}{2\pi\iota}\frac{\pi}{2}\frac{a}{c}\int_L I_0'\left(\frac{\lambda a}{c}\right) K_0\left(\frac{\lambda\varpi}{c}\right) e^{\lambda t}\frac{d\lambda}{\lambda}. \qquad \text{.........(6)}\end{aligned}$$

But

$$I_0(z) = \frac{1}{\pi}\int_0^\pi \exp(z\cos\theta)\, d\theta, \qquad \text{.................(7)}$$

$$K_0(z) = \frac{2}{\pi}\int_0^\infty \exp(-z\cosh v)\, dv, \qquad \text{...............(8)}$$

whence

$$\frac{\rho\Phi}{P_0} = -\frac{a}{2\pi^2\iota c}\int_L\int_0^\pi\int_0^\infty \frac{1}{\lambda}\exp\lambda\left(t + \frac{a}{c}\cos\theta - \frac{\varpi}{c}\cosh v\right)\cos\theta\, d\lambda\, d\theta\, dv. \qquad \text{......(9)}$$

Performing first the integration with regard to λ, we obtain a function of the form $H(t-b)$. Thus

$$\frac{\rho\Phi}{P_0} = -\frac{a}{\pi c}\int_0^\pi\int_0^\infty \cos\theta\, d\theta\, dv, \qquad \text{..................(10)}$$

where the range of integration is restricted by the condition that

$$ct + a\cos\theta - \varpi\cosh v > 0. \qquad \text{..................(11)}$$

It follows at once that there is no movement at a place until time $(\varpi - a)/c$. Integrating next with regard to v, we see that the admissible values range from 0 to $\cosh^{-1}\{(ct + a\cos\theta)/\varpi\}$, provided the quantity in the parentheses is greater than unity. Hence

$$\frac{\rho\Phi}{P_0} = -\frac{a}{\pi c}\int \cos\theta\cosh^{-1}\left(\frac{ct + a\cos\theta}{\varpi}\right) d\theta. \qquad \text{.........(12)}$$

So long as $ct > \varpi - a$, there will be a finite range of integration with regard to θ; the lower limit is then always zero. If $ct > \varpi + a$, the inequality is satisfied for all values of θ up to π, and therefore π is the upper limit. If $ct < \varpi + a$, the inequality is not satisfied when $\theta = \pi$, and the upper limit is $\cos^{-1}(\varpi - ct)/a$. The disturbance at any point may therefore be divided into three stages, the first until $ct = \varpi - a$, the second from then till $ct = \varpi + a$, and the third later.

We are concerned chiefly with the pressure. This remains constant until $ct = \varpi - a$; in the next stage

$$\frac{P}{P_0} = \frac{a}{\pi}\int_0^{\cos^{-1}(\varpi - ct)/a} \frac{\cos\theta\, d\theta}{\{(ct + a\cos\theta)^2 - \varpi^2\}^{\frac{1}{2}}} \quad \text{............(13)}$$

and in the last a similar integral with the upper limit replaced by π. By applying the transformation

$$ct + a - \varpi = 2b; \quad ct + a\cos\theta - \varpi = 2b\cos^2\psi \quad \text{........(14)}$$

and integrating on the supposition that b is small, we find that soon after the arrival of the wave

$$\frac{P}{P_0} = \tfrac{1}{2}\sqrt{\left(\frac{a}{\varpi}\right)}\left[1 - \frac{3}{4}\frac{b}{a} - \frac{1}{4}\frac{b}{\varpi}\right]. \quad \text{...........(15)}$$

When the wave arrives the pressure therefore jumps to $\tfrac{1}{2}P_0(a/\varpi)$, and then falls by $\dfrac{c}{8}\left(\dfrac{3}{a} + \dfrac{1}{\varpi}\right)$ of itself per unit time. The corresponding fraction in the spherical problem is c/a. At time ϖ/c the pressure is still positive; but when $ct = \varpi + a$ or more and θ is greater than $\tfrac{1}{2}\pi$, the integrand in (13) is numerically greater than for the supplementary value of θ, and thus P is negative. It actually tends to $-\infty$ at $ct = \varpi + a$, and returns to finite negative values for greater values of t. The passage of the wave of rarefaction is therefore indefinitely protracted. To find out how it dies down with the time let us suppose that ct is greater than ϖ, and that a is small compared with either. Then

$$P = -\tfrac{1}{2}P_0\frac{a^2 ct}{(c^2t^2 - \varpi^2)^{\frac{3}{2}}} \quad \text{...................(16)}$$

approximately. The residual disturbance falls off like t^{-2}.

6.22. If the motion was one-dimensional, as for instance if the original excess of pressure was confined to a length $2a$ of a tube, the resulting disturbance of pressure would consist of two waves, each with an excess of pressure equal to $\tfrac{1}{2}P_0$, travelling out in opposite directions with velocity c. Comparing the results for the three cases, we see that the first disturbance at a given point outside the region originally disturbed, in each case at the same distance from the nearest point of it, occurs in each case at the same moment. The increase of pressure in the one-dimensional problem is $\frac{1}{2}P_0$, in the two-dimensional one $\frac{1}{2}P_0(a/\varpi)^{\frac{1}{2}}$, and in the three-dimensional one $\frac{1}{2}P_0(a/r)$. In the first case the pressure remains constant for time $2a/c$, and then drops to zero and remains there. In the cylindrical problem it begins to fall instantly, and becomes negative in an interval less than $2a/c$; it tends to $-\infty$, and dies down again asymptotically to zero. In the spherical one it decreases linearly with the time and reaches a negative value equal to the original positive one at time $2a/c$; then it suddenly becomes zero again.

6.3. *Diverging waves produced by a sphere oscillating radially**. Suppose that a sphere of radius a begins at time 0 to oscillate radially in period $2\pi/n$. We require the motion of the air outside it.

The velocity potential Φ satisfies the equation

$$\frac{\partial^2}{\partial r^2}(r\Phi) - \frac{\partial^2}{c^2\partial t^2}(r\Phi) = 0. \quad \text{......(1)}$$

Initially all is at rest; the solution is therefore

$$r\Phi = Ae^{-pr/c}. \quad \text{......(2)}$$

When $r=a$ the outward displacement is, say, $\frac{1}{n}\sin nt$ when $t>0$, and the outward velocity $\cos nt$. Hence

$$A\left[\frac{\partial}{\partial r}\left(\frac{1}{r}e^{-pr/c}\right)\right]_{r=a} = \frac{p^2}{p^2+n^2} \quad \text{......(3)}$$

and

$$r\Phi = -\frac{p^2a^2}{(p^2+n^2)(1+pa/c)}\exp\left\{-\frac{p}{c}(r-a)\right\}$$

$$= -\frac{c^2a^2}{c^2+a^2n^2}\exp\left\{-\frac{p}{c}(r-a)\right\}\left\{\cos nt + \frac{na}{c}\sin nt - \exp\left(-\frac{ct}{a}\right)\right\}$$

$$= -\frac{c^2a^2}{c^2+a^2n^2}\left[\cos n\left\{t-\frac{r-a}{c}\right\} + \frac{na}{c}\sin n\left\{t-\frac{r-a}{c}\right\} - \exp\left\{-\frac{ct-r+a}{a}\right\}\right] \quad \text{......(4)}$$

when $ct>r-a$.

The solution has a periodic part with a period equal to that of the given disturbance, together with a part dying down with the time at a rate independent of n, but involving the size of the sphere. As there is no corresponding term in the problem of 6.2 we may regard it as a result of the constraint introduced by the presence of the rigid sphere.

* Love, *Proc. Lond. Math. Soc.* (2) 2, 1904, 88; Bromwich, *ib.* (2) 15, 1916, 431.

Its effect on the velocity or the pressure is to that of the second term in a ratio comparable with $(c/na)^2$.

6.4. A spherical thermometer bulb is initially at a uniform temperature equal to that of its surroundings. The temperature of the air decreases with height, and the thermometer is carried upwards at such a rate that the temperature at the outside of the glass varies linearly with the time. Find how the mean temperature of the mercury varies*.

The temperature within the bulb satisfies the equation

$$\frac{\partial^2}{\partial r^2}(rV) - q^2 rV = 0, \qquad \text{.........(1)}$$

where

$$p = h^2 q^2. \qquad \text{.........(2)}$$

That at the outer surface of the glass is Gt, where G is a constant. But the glass has only a finite conductivity, so that the surface condition at the outside of the mercury is

$$\frac{\partial V}{\partial r} = K(Gt - V), \qquad \text{.........(3)}$$

K being another constant. The solution of (1) is

$$V = \frac{A}{r}\sinh qr \qquad \text{.........(4)}$$

and (3) gives

$$A = \frac{a^2 KG/p}{Ka\sinh qa + qa\cosh qa - \sinh qa}, \qquad \text{.........(5)}$$

where a is the inner radius of the glass.

The mean temperature within the bulb is

$$\begin{aligned} V_0 &= \frac{3}{a^3}\int_0^a r^2 V\,dr \\ &= \frac{3A}{a^3 q^2}(qa\cosh qa - \sinh qa) \\ &= \frac{3KG}{apq^2}\,\frac{qa\cosh qa - \sinh qa}{Ka\sinh qa + qa\cosh qa - \sinh qa}. \qquad \text{.........(6)} \end{aligned}$$

In applying the partial-fraction rule, we notice that near $p = 0$

$$\begin{aligned} V_0 &= \frac{3KG}{apq^2}\,\frac{(qa)^3\left(\frac{1}{3} + \frac{1}{30}q^2a^2\right)}{qa\left(Ka + \frac{1}{6}Kq^2a^3 + \frac{1}{3}q^2a^2\right)} \\ &= G\left\{\frac{1}{p} - \left(\frac{1}{15}\frac{a^2}{h^2} + \frac{1}{3}\frac{a}{h^2K}\right)\right\} \\ &= G\left\{t - \frac{a^2}{h^2}\left(\frac{1}{15} + \frac{1}{3aK}\right)\right\}, \end{aligned}$$

* Bromwich, *Phil. Mag.* 37, 1919, 407–419; A. R. McLeod, *Phil. Mag.* 37, 1919, 134.

so that there is a constant lag in the temperature of the mercury in comparison with that of the air.

The other zeros of the denominator give exponential contributions, which are evaluated in Bromwich's paper.

6.5. A cylinder of internal radius a can rotate freely about its axis. It is filled with viscous liquid, and the whole is rotating as if solid with angular velocity ω_0. The cylinder is instantaneously brought to rest at time $t=0$, and immediately released. Find the angular velocity later. (Math. Trip. Schedule B, 1926.)

The motion is two-dimensional, and there is a stream-function ψ satisfying the equation

$$\left(\nu\nabla^2-\frac{\partial}{\partial t}\right)\nabla^2\psi=\frac{\partial(\psi,\nabla^2\psi)}{\partial(x,y)}, \quad \text{.................(1)}$$

where ν is the kinematic viscosity. Since the motion is symmetrical about an axis the right side is identically zero. Put

$$\frac{\partial}{\partial t}=p, \quad p=\nu r^2, \quad \nabla^2=\frac{1}{\varpi}\frac{\partial}{\partial\varpi}\left(\varpi\frac{\partial}{\partial\varpi}\right). \quad \text{...........(2)}$$

Initially $$\psi=\tfrac{1}{2}\varpi^2\omega_0; \quad \nabla^2\psi=2\omega_0 \quad \text{.......................(3)}$$

and the subsidiary equation is

$$(\nabla^2-r^2)\nabla^2\psi=-2r^2\omega_0. \quad \text{.....................(4)}$$

The solution is

$$\psi=AI_0(r\varpi)+BK_0(r\varpi)+C\log\varpi+D+\tfrac{1}{2}\varpi^2\omega_0. \quad \text{......(5)}$$

The velocity must be finite on the axis; hence B and C are zero. Also D is independent of ϖ and therefore cannot affect the motion.

If I be the moment of inertia of the cylinder per unit length and ω its angular velocity, the equation of motion of the cylinder is

$$I\frac{\partial\omega}{\partial t}=-2\pi a p_s, \quad \text{.........................(6)}$$

where p_s is the shearing stress in the fluid. Now

$$p_s=\nu\rho\left(\frac{\partial^2\psi}{\partial x^2}-\frac{\partial^2\psi}{\partial y^2}\right)$$

$$=\nu\rho a\frac{\partial}{\partial\varpi}\left(\frac{1}{\varpi}\frac{\partial\psi}{\partial\varpi}\right) \quad \text{.......................(7)}$$

evaluated on the outer boundary at the point $(a, 0)$. Hence

$$p_s=\nu\rho\frac{A}{a}r\,[raI_0(ra)-2I_0'(ra)]. \quad \text{...............(8)}$$

Since the cylinder starts from rest,

$$I p\omega = -2\pi\nu\rho\, A r\,[ra\, I_0(ra) - 2I_0'(ra)]. \quad \text{............(9)}$$

Also $a\omega$ must be equal to the velocity of the fluid. Hence

$$a\omega = A r\, I_0'(ra) + a\omega_0. \quad \text{.....................(10)}$$

Eliminating A we have

$$\omega\,[(Kp-2)\, I_0'(ra) + ra\, I_0(ra)] = \omega_0\,[ra\, I_0(ra) - 2I_0'(ra)], \text{...(11)}$$

where

$$2\pi\nu\rho a K = I. \quad \text{..........................(12)}$$

The operational solution is therefore

$$\omega = \omega_0 \frac{ra\, I_0(ra) - 2I_0'(ra)}{(Kp-2)\, I_0'(ra) + ra\, I_0(ra)}. \quad \text{............(13)}$$

But

$$I_0(ra) = 1 + \tfrac{1}{4}r^2a^2 + \tfrac{1}{64}r^4a^4 + \ldots;\; I_0'(ra) = \tfrac{1}{2}ra + \tfrac{1}{16}r^3a^3 + \ldots. \text{ (14)}$$

The contribution from $p=0$ is found to be

$$\frac{\omega_0 a^2}{a^2 + 4\nu K} = \omega_1, \quad \text{..........................(15)}$$

say. This is the ultimate angular velocity. The other terms arise from the zeros of the denominator. If we write ιk for r, and substitute for K in terms of ω_1, we find that these satisfy

$$\left\{(\omega_0 - \omega_1)\frac{a^2k^2}{4\omega_1} + 2\right\} J_1(ka) - ka\, J_0(ka) = 0.$$

The solution is then of the form $\omega_1 + \Sigma A_k e^{-k^2\nu t}$. The coefficients A_k are determinable by the usual method.

CHAPTER VII

DISPERSION

In the propagation of sound waves in air and of waves on strings the velocity of travel of waves is independent of the period. In many problems this is not the case; waves on water afford an important example.

7.1. Consider a layer of incompressible fluid of density ρ and depth H. Take the origin in the undisturbed position of the free surface, the axis of z upwards, and those of x and y in the horizontal plane. Put

$$\frac{\partial}{\partial t} = p;\; \frac{\partial}{\partial x} = D;\; \frac{\partial}{\partial y} = D';\; \frac{\partial^2}{\partial x^2} + \frac{\partial^2}{\partial y^2} = r^2. \quad \text{...........(1)}$$

The velocity potential Φ satisfies the equation

$$\frac{\partial^2 \Phi}{\partial z^2} + r^2 \Phi = 0. \qquad \text{.............................(2)}$$

At the bottom the vertical velocity vanishes. At the free surface, so long as the motion is only slightly disturbed from rest, we have

$$\frac{\partial \Phi}{\partial z} = \frac{\partial \zeta}{\partial t}, \qquad \text{.............................(3)}$$

where ζ is the elevation of the free surface. Then we must have

$$\Phi = -\frac{p}{r} \frac{\cos r(z+H)}{\sin rH} \zeta. \qquad \text{....................(4)}$$

The pressure just under the free surface is $-T\rho r^2 \zeta$, where $T\rho$ is the surface tension. But by Bernoulli's equation it is also equal to

$$-\rho p \Phi - g\rho \zeta + F(t),$$

and $F(t)$ does not affect the motion and can therefore be omitted. We have therefore the further surface condition

$$-p\Phi = (g - Tr^2)\zeta. \qquad \text{......................(5)}$$

Combining this with (4) we have the differential equation for ζ

$$\{p^2 - (g - Tr^2) r \tan rH\} \zeta = 0. \qquad \text{.................(6)}$$

If the fluid starts from rest with ζ equal to ζ_0, a known function of x and y, the subsidiary equation will have a term $p^2 \zeta_0$ on the right, and the operational solution will be

$$\zeta = \frac{p^2}{p^2 - (g - Tr^2) r \tan rH} \zeta_0 \qquad \text{......................(7)}$$

$$= \cosh t \{(g - Tr^2) r \tan rH\}^{\frac{1}{2}} . \zeta_0. \qquad \text{..............(8)}$$

In the corresponding problem of a uniform string in 4.1 the coefficient of t was simply pc. This solution, like d'Alembert's solution for the string, assumes that there are no ends to reflect waves.

Suppose first that the original disturbance consists of an infinite elevation along the axis of y, with no disturbance of the surface anywhere else. Then ζ_0 can be replaced by $DH(x)$, and (8) is equivalent to the integral

$$\zeta = \frac{1}{2\pi\iota} \int_L e^{\kappa x} \cosh t \{(g - T\kappa^2) \kappa \tan \kappa H\}^{\frac{1}{2}} d\kappa. \qquad \text{........(9)}$$

The integrand has an essential singularity wherever κH is an odd multiple of $\frac{1}{2}\pi$; L cannot therefore cross the real axis within a finite distance of the origin, but becomes two branches extending to $+\infty$ above and below the axis.

7.2. *The method of steepest descents.* The elevation of the surface is thus expressed in terms of integrals of the type

$$S = \int_A^B \exp t\{f(z)\}\, dz, \quad \text{.....................(1)}$$

where $f(z)$ is an analytic function, and t is real, positive, and independent of z. Put, following Debye,

$$f(z) = R + \iota I, \quad \text{..........................(2)}$$

thus expressing it in real and imaginary parts. If the integral is taken along an arbitrary path, the integrand will be the product of a variable positive factor with one whose absolute value is unity, but which varies in argument more and more rapidly the greater t is. There will evidently be advantages in choosing the path in such a way that the large values of R are concentrated in the shortest possible interval on it. Now if

$$z = x + \iota y, \quad \text{............................(3)}$$

we shall have

$$\frac{\partial^2 R}{\partial x^2} + \frac{\partial^2 R}{\partial y^2} = 0; \; \frac{\partial^2 I}{\partial x^2} + \frac{\partial^2 I}{\partial y^2} = 0. \quad \text{..................(4)}$$

It follows that R can never be an absolute maximum. But it can have stationary points, where

$$\frac{\partial R}{\partial x} = \frac{\partial R}{\partial y} = 0, \quad \text{..............................(5)}$$

and we know that these points will also be stationary points of I and zeros of $f'(z)$. These points are usually called the 'saddle-points,' or sometimes 'cols.' Through any saddle-point it will in general be possible to draw two (sometimes more) curves such that R is constant along them. In sectors between these curves R will be alternately greater and less than at the saddle-point itself. The sectors where R is greater may be called the 'hills,' those where it is less the 'valleys.' If our path of integration is to be chosen so as to avoid large values of R, it must avoid the hills, and keep as far as possible to the valleys. If then the complex plane is marked out by the lines of R constant through all the saddle-points, and A and B lie within the same valley, our path must never go outside this valley; but if A and B lie in different valleys, the passage from one valley to another must take place through a saddle-point. In the latter case the value of the integral will be much greater than in the former, and therefore interest attaches chiefly to the case where the limits of the integral lie in different valleys.

The paths actually chosen are specified rather more narrowly; the direction of the path at any point is chosen so that $|\partial R/\partial s|$ is as great as possible. If ψ is the inclination of the tangent to the path to the axis of x, we have

$$\frac{\partial R}{\partial s} = \cos\psi \frac{\partial R}{\partial x} + \sin\psi \frac{\partial R}{\partial y}, \quad \text{......................(6)}$$

and if this is to be a numerical maximum for variations in ψ

$$0 = -\sin\psi \frac{\partial R}{\partial x} + \cos\psi \frac{\partial R}{\partial y}$$

$$= \frac{\partial R}{\partial n} = \frac{\partial I}{\partial s}, \quad \text{......................................(7)}$$

where dn is an element of length normal to the path, drawn so that when ds is in the direction of x increasing, dn is in the direction of y increasing. Hence I is constant along the path. Such a path is called a 'line of steepest descent.' There will be one in each valley. In general the limits of the integral will not themselves lie on lines of steepest descent, but can be joined to them by paths within the valleys.

In general lines of R constant through different saddle-points will not intersect; and there will be only one saddle-point on each line of steepest descent. For the former event would imply that R has the same value at two saddle-points, the latter that I has, and either of these events will be exceptional. It follows that as we proceed along a line of steepest descent R will rarely reach a minimum and then proceed to increase again. For if R had a minimum $\partial R/\partial s$ would be zero; but $\partial I/\partial s$ is zero by construction, and therefore the point would be another saddle-point. Lines of steepest descent usually terminate only at singularities of $f(z)$ or at infinity.

The path of integration once chosen, the greater t is the more closely the higher values of the integrand will be concentrated about the saddle-points. Thus we can obtain an approximation, which will be better the larger t is, by considering only the parts of the path in these regions. In these conditions we can take

$$f(z) = f(z_0) + \tfrac{1}{2}(z - z_0)^2 f''(z_0), \quad \text{..................(8)}$$

where z_0 is a saddle-point. Put

$$|f''(z_0)| = A; \quad |z - z_0| = r. \quad \text{.....................(9)}$$

Then on a line of steepest descent

$$f(z) = f(z_0) - \tfrac{1}{2}Ar^2, \quad \text{.....................(10)}$$

and we can put

$$\arg(z - z_0) = \alpha \quad \text{.......................(11)}$$

on the side after passing through z_0. Then

$$S = 2\int_0^\infty \exp\{tf(z_0)\}\exp(-\tfrac{1}{2}Atr^2)\,d(r\exp\iota\alpha)$$

$$= \left(\frac{2\pi}{At}\right)^{\frac{1}{2}} \exp\{tf(z_0) + \iota\alpha\}, \quad \text{.................................(12)}$$

the approach to z_0 and the descent from it making equal contributions.

To get from A to B it may be necessary to pass through two or more saddle-points, with probably traverses in the valleys between the lines of steepest descent. Then each saddle-point will make its contribution to the integral.

The error involved in this approximation arises from the terms of the third and higher orders omitted from (8). Its accuracy therefore depends on $\exp(-\frac{1}{2}tAr^2)$ having become small before $\exp(-\frac{1}{6}tr^3|f'''(z_0)|)$ has begun to differ appreciably from unity. Hence

$$\tfrac{1}{2}tA\left[\frac{6}{t|f'''(z_0)|}\right]^{\frac{2}{3}} = 1{\cdot}6\,t^{\frac{1}{3}}\frac{|f''(z_0)|}{|f'''(z_0)|^{\frac{2}{3}}} \quad \text{.........(13)}$$

must be large. In most cases the approximation is asymptotic, and does not represent the first term of a convergent series.

7.3. In problems of wave motion we often have to evaluate integrals of the form

$$\zeta = \frac{1}{2\pi\iota}\int_L \phi(\kappa)\exp(\kappa x - \gamma t)\,d\kappa, \quad \text{..................(1)}$$

where $\phi(\kappa)$ and γ are known functions of κ. As a rule $\phi(\kappa)$ is an even function, and γ an odd one. When κ is purely imaginary γ is also purely imaginary. We require the motion for large values of t, and possibly also of x.

The function $\phi(\kappa)$ usually introduces no difficulty. It does not involve x or t, and therefore when these are large enough it can be treated as constant throughout the range where the integrand is appreciable.

It is usually convenient to replace κ by $\iota\kappa$ and γ by $\iota\gamma$, and to consider the equivalent integral of the form

$$\zeta = \frac{1}{2\pi}\int_{-\infty}^{\infty} \psi(\kappa)\exp\iota(\kappa x - \gamma t)\,d\kappa. \quad \text{.................(2)}$$

The saddle-points are given by

$$x - \gamma' t = 0, \quad \text{.............................(3)}$$

so that a given ratio x/t specifies a set of predominant values of κ_0. But γ' is an even function of κ, and therefore if κ_0 is a saddle-point, $-\kappa_0$ will be another, and if the adopted path passes through either it will pass through the other. We may take κ_0 real and positive. Also

$$f''(\kappa_0) = -\iota\gamma_0'' t. \qquad \text{(4)}$$

Thus if γ_0'' is positive $\kappa - \kappa_0$ has argument $-\frac{1}{4}\pi$ on the line of steepest descent, and the contribution from κ_0 is

$$\frac{1}{2\pi}\left(\frac{2\pi}{|\gamma_0'' t|}\right)^{\frac{1}{2}} \psi(\kappa_0)\, e^{-\frac{1}{4}\iota\pi} \exp \iota(\kappa_0 x - \gamma_0 t). \qquad \text{(5)}$$

The contribution from $-\kappa_0$ (where γ'' is negative) is similarly

$$\frac{1}{2\pi}\left(\frac{2\pi}{|\gamma_0'' t|}\right)^{\frac{1}{2}} \psi(\kappa_0)\, e^{\frac{1}{4}\iota\pi} \exp\{-\iota(\kappa_0 x - \gamma_0 t)\}, \qquad \text{(6)}$$

and the two together give

$$\left(\frac{2}{\pi|\gamma_0'' t|}\right)^{\frac{1}{2}} \psi(\kappa_0) \cos(\kappa_0 x - \gamma_0 t - \tfrac{1}{4}\pi). \qquad \text{(7)}$$

Similarly if γ_0'' is negative the two saddle-points give

$$\left(\frac{2}{\pi|\gamma_0'' t|}\right)^{\frac{1}{2}} \psi(\kappa_0) \cos(\kappa_0 x - \gamma_0 t + \tfrac{1}{4}\pi). \qquad \text{(8)}$$

7.31. These formulae, due to Kelvin, are the fundamental ones of the theory of dispersion. Consider first the cosine factor, and suppose x increased by δx and t by δt. Then $\kappa_0 x - \gamma_0 t$ is increased by

$$\kappa_0 \delta x - \gamma_0 \delta t + (x - \gamma_0' t)\,\delta\kappa_0,$$

the term in $\delta\kappa_0$ appearing because κ_0 is defined as a function of x and t by (3). But the coefficient of $\delta\kappa_0$ is zero by (3). If then t is kept constant, ζ will vary with x with period $2\pi/\kappa_0$; and if x is kept constant, ζ will vary with t with period $2\pi/\gamma_0$. Hence $2\pi/\kappa_0$ is the wave-length, and $2\pi/\gamma_0$ the period, of the waves passing a given place. A phase occurring at a given place and time is reproduced after an interval δt at a place such that $\delta x = \gamma_0\, \delta t/\kappa_0$. Hence γ_0/κ_0 is the velocity of travel of individual waves. It may be denoted by c, and called the wave-velocity.

But κ_0 has been defined by the equation

$$x - \gamma_0' t = 0,$$

so that a given wave-length and period always occur when x/t has a particular value; they seem to travel out with velocity γ_0', which is called the group-velocity. It may also be denoted by C. In general the wave-velocity and the group-velocity are unequal, so that a given wave changes in period and length as it progresses. They are evidently connected by the relation

$$\frac{\partial}{\partial\kappa}(\kappa c) = C. \qquad \text{(9)}$$

7.4. Returning now to 7.1 (9) we can separate the hyperbolic function into two exponentials, which will represent wave-systems travelling out in opposite directions. One of them is equivalent to

$$\zeta = \frac{1}{4\pi}\int_{-\infty}^{\infty} \exp \iota(\kappa x - \gamma t)\, d\kappa, \qquad \text{.................(1)}$$

where $$\gamma^2 = (g + T\kappa^2)\,\kappa \tanh \kappa H. \qquad \text{.....................(2)}$$

When κ is small,

$$c = (gH)^{\frac{1}{2}}\left(1 - \tfrac{1}{6}\kappa^2 H^2 + \frac{1}{2}\frac{T\kappa^2}{g}\right), \text{.................(3)}$$

$$C = (gH)^{\frac{1}{2}}\left(1 - \tfrac{1}{2}\kappa^2 H^2 + \frac{3}{2}\frac{T\kappa^2}{g}\right). \text{.................(4)}$$

When κ is great,

$$c = (T\kappa)^{\frac{1}{2}};\; C = \tfrac{3}{2}(T\kappa)^{\frac{1}{2}}. \qquad \text{....................(5)}$$

In all ordinary cases T/g is insignificant in comparison with H^2. Hence for some intermediate value of κ the group-velocity is a minimum; it tends to infinity for very short waves, and to a finite limit for very long ones. Three cases therefore arise. If x/t is less than the minimum group-velocity, there will be no saddle-point on the real axis, and the disturbance will be small*. If it lies between this minimum and $(gH)^{\frac{1}{2}}$, two (positive) values of κ will give saddle-points, and each will contribute to the motion. If it is greater than $(gH)^{\frac{1}{2}}$, the only saddle-point will correspond to a short wave. The disturbance at a given point will therefore be in three stages. In the first, leading up to time $x/(gH)^{\frac{1}{2}}$, only very short capillary waves will occur. Then long gravity waves will arrive, the wave-lengths of those reaching the point diminishing as time goes on. Superposed on them are further capillary waves, their length increasing with the time. At a certain moment the wave-lengths of the two sets become equal. This corresponds to the arrival of the waves with the minimum group-velocity. From then on the water is smooth.

7.41. Two typical cases therefore arise according as the wave-length is large or small compared with the one that gives the minimum group-velocity. Take first gravity waves, such that x/t is small compared with

* It can be shown that the saddle-points are so placed that the relevant one contributes an exponential with a negative index to the solution. This is almost obvious from considerations of energy.

$(gH)^{\frac{1}{2}}$ but large compared with the minimum group-velocity. In these conditions we can write simply

$$\gamma^2 = g\kappa;\ c = (g/\kappa)^{\frac{1}{2}};\ C = \tfrac{1}{2}(g/\kappa)^{\frac{1}{2}};\ dC/d\kappa = -\tfrac{1}{4}(g/\kappa^3)^{\frac{1}{2}}. \quad \ldots(1)$$

The solution is then

$$\left(\frac{1}{2\pi t}\right)^{\frac{1}{2}} 2 \left(\frac{\kappa_0^3}{g}\right)^{\frac{1}{4}} \cos(\kappa_0 x - \gamma_0 t + \tfrac{1}{4}\pi), \quad \ldots\ldots\ldots\ldots(2)$$

where

$$\frac{x}{t} = \frac{1}{2}\left(\frac{g}{\kappa_0}\right)^{\frac{1}{2}} \quad \ldots\ldots\ldots\ldots(3)$$

and the amplitude increases towards the rear of the wave train like $x^{-\frac{3}{2}}$.

7.42. Take next the capillary waves, short enough for gravity to be neglected. Then

$$\gamma^2 = T\kappa^3;\ c = (T\kappa)^{\frac{1}{2}};\ C = \tfrac{3}{2}(T\kappa)^{\frac{1}{2}};\ dC/d\kappa = \tfrac{3}{4}(T/\kappa)^{\frac{1}{2}}. \quad \ldots\ldots(1)$$

At a given instant the amplitude is therefore proportional to $\kappa_0^{\frac{1}{4}}$, or to $x^{\frac{1}{2}}$. The front of the disturbance is therefore composed of a series of capillary waves whose amplitude tends to infinity, and the time taken for them to arrive is infinitesimal.

This impossible result arises from the form assumed for the original displacement. In taking $\zeta_0 = DH(x)$ we assumed that unit volume of liquid was originally released on unit length of the actual line $x = 0$ in the surface. The mean height of this mass of liquid was therefore infinite, and its potential energy also infinite. The system being frictionless, this energy must be present somewhere in the waves existing at any instant, and infinite amplitudes are therefore a natural consequence of the initial conditions. If instead we suppose that the same volume of fluid was originally raised, but that it was distributed uniformly between $x = \pm l$, its elevation was $1/2l$ in this range. Expressed in operational form this gives

$$\zeta_0 = \frac{1}{2l}[H(x+l) - H(x-l)] = \frac{1}{2l}(e^{pl} - e^{-pl}). \quad \ldots\ldots\ldots(2)$$

The appropriate solution can be found from 7.4 (1) by introducing a factor $\frac{1}{2l\iota\kappa}(e^{\iota\kappa l} - e^{-\iota\kappa l})$ or $\frac{\sin \kappa l}{\kappa l}$ into the integrand. If the solution already found makes $\kappa_0 l$ small, this additional factor will be practically unity, and the same solution will hold. Waves whose length is large compared with the extent of the original disturbance will therefore not be much affected by its finiteness.

But if $\kappa_0 l$ is large we must consider separately the contributions from the terms in $e^{\iota\kappa l}$ and $e^{-\iota\kappa l}$. The factor $1/\kappa l$ will give an extra $1/\kappa_0 l$ in all the solutions. The result will be that at a given instant the amplitude of a gravity wave will vary like $\kappa_0^{-\frac{1}{4}}$ and that of a capillary wave like $\kappa_0^{-\frac{3}{4}}$. Waves whose length is short compared with that of the original disturbance are therefore heavily reduced in amplitude.

On deep water the minimum group-velocity is 18 cm./sec., corresponding to a wave-length of 4·6 cm. and a wave-velocity of 28 cm./sec. If the original disturbance has a horizontal extent of 1 cm. or so, only waves with lengths under 1 cm. or so will be affected, and the amplitudes of both gravity and capillary waves will increase steadily with diminishing group-velocity. A wave of large amplitude will therefore bring up the rear, and will leave smooth water behind it. This is observable in the waves caused by raindrops and other very concentrated disturbances. But if the extent of the original disturbance exceeds a few centimetres the capillary waves produced will be very small, and the largest amplitude will be associated with a wave whose length is comparable with the width of the disturbed region. The largest wave produced by the splash of a brick, for instance, has a length of the order of a foot.

7.5. Two exceptional cases may arise in the treatment of dispersion, which are both illustrated in the present problem. The validity of the approximation 7.2 (12) depends on $\exp\{tf(z)\}$ being proportional to $\exp(-\frac{1}{2}Atr^2)$ on a line of steepest descent. If $f''(z)$ has varied by a considerable fraction of A before this exponential has become small the approximation will not be good. This may happen if A is itself small, or if there are two saddle-points close together. Instances occur when there is a maximum or minimum group-velocity, or if the group-velocity tends to a finite limit when κ becomes very small. In the former case a value of x/t a little greater than the minimum group-velocity will give two slightly different finite values of κ_0. In the latter κ_0 may be small enough for the proximity of $-\kappa_0$ to affect the contributions of both.

7.51. Since γ is an odd function of κ, we may suppose that when κ is small

$$\gamma = c_0\kappa - c_2\kappa^3 + O(\kappa^5) \quad \text{.......................(1)}$$

and then 7.3 (2) is equivalent to

$$\zeta = \frac{1}{2\pi}\int_{-\infty}^{\infty} \psi(\kappa)\exp\iota(\kappa x - c_0\kappa t + c_2\kappa^3 t)\,d\kappa. \quad \text{........(2)}$$

There are saddle-points where

$$\kappa = \pm \left(\frac{c_0 t - x}{3c_2 t}\right)^{\frac{1}{2}}. \quad \text{.........................(3)}$$

If, as in 7.3, $\psi(\kappa)$ is constant or tends to a limit different from zero when κ tends to zero, this integral is nearly

$$\zeta = \frac{1}{\pi}\int_0^\infty \psi(0)\cos\{\kappa(x - c_0 t) + c_2\kappa^3 t\}\, d\kappa$$

$$= \frac{1}{\pi}\psi(0)\,(c_2 t)^{-\frac{1}{3}}\int_0^\infty \cos(v^3 - mv)\, dv, \quad \text{..............(4)}$$

where $$m = (c_0 t - x)/(c_2 t)^{\frac{1}{3}}. \quad \text{.......................(5)}$$

The integral involved here is called an Airy integral*. It is finite and positive, but not stationary, when $m = 0$; it has a maximum when $m = 1{\cdot}28$, and oscillates for greater values of m with steadily decreasing amplitude. For negative values of m it tends asymptotically to zero.

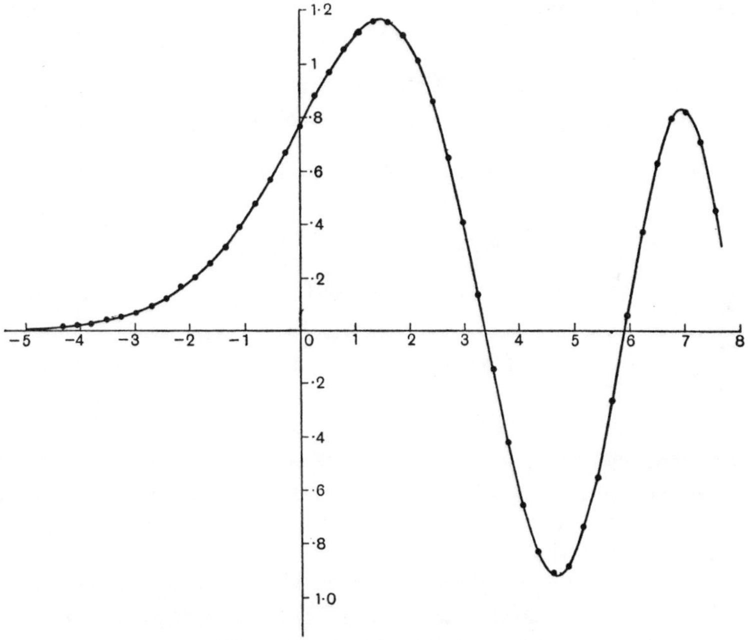

Fig. 7. Graph of the Airy integral.

* Airy tabulates $\int_0^\infty \cos \tfrac{1}{2}\pi(v^3 - mv)\, dv$ in *Camb. Phil. Trans.* 8, 1849, 598. The graph given here is adapted from Airy's table. The integral can also be expressed in terms of Bessel functions of order $\pm\frac{1}{3}$. See Watson, 188–190.

Consequently the disturbance we are considering produces an immediate rise of the level of the water at all distances greater than $c_0 t$, though this rise is very small at great distances. The maximum rise of level is where x is rather less than $c_0 t$, so that it has not travelled out from the origin so far as a wave with the limiting velocity would. The maximum is followed by a series of waves of gradually diminishing length and amplitude, merging ultimately into gravity waves of the deep-water type.

7.52. In the case where there is a minimum group-velocity for a finite wave-length, let us, with a somewhat different notation from that used so far, denote the minimum group-velocity by γ_0' and the corresponding values of κ and γ by κ_0 and γ_0. Put

$$\kappa - \kappa_0 = \kappa_1, \qquad \text{.........(1)}$$

$$\gamma = \gamma_0 + \gamma_0'\kappa_1 + 0 + \tfrac{1}{6}\gamma_0'''\kappa_1^3 + \dots \qquad \text{.........(2)}$$

Then

$$\zeta = \frac{1}{2\pi}\int_{-\kappa_0}^{\infty} \psi(\kappa) \exp \iota(\kappa_0 x - \gamma_0 t) \exp \iota(\kappa_1 x - \gamma_0'\kappa_1 t - \tfrac{1}{6}\gamma_0'''\kappa_1^3 t)\, d\kappa_1 \ldots(3)$$

with an analogous contribution from the negative values of κ; hence with the same type of approximation as before we shall have

$$\zeta = \frac{2}{\pi}\int_0^{\infty} \psi(\kappa_0) \cos(\kappa_0 x - \gamma_0 t) \cos(\kappa_1 x - \gamma_0'\kappa_1 t - \tfrac{1}{6}\gamma_0'''\kappa_1^3 t)\, d\kappa_1$$

$$= \frac{2}{\pi}\psi(\kappa_0)\cos(\kappa_0 x - \gamma_0 t)(\tfrac{1}{6}\gamma_0''' t)^{-\frac{1}{3}} \int_0^{\infty} \cos(v^3 - mv)\, dv, \quad \ldots(4)$$

where

$$m = \frac{x - \gamma_0' t}{(\tfrac{1}{6}\gamma_0''' t)^{\frac{1}{3}}}. \qquad \text{.........(5)}$$

The solution is therefore the product of a cosine and an Airy integral, the interval between consecutive zeros being much greater for the former than for the latter. In the neighbourhood of a point that has travelled out with the minimum group-velocity the waves have the corresponding period and wave-length, but their amplitude falls off rapidly towards the rear. In front of this point the amplitude increases for a while and then oscillates.

In both these exceptional cases we notice that the amplitude associated with the critical velocity falls off only like the inverse cube root of the time, whereas in the typical case it falls off like the inverse square root. Hence the further the disturbance progresses the more will the waves with the critical group-velocities predominate in relation to the others. In waves on water, however, these phenomena are often modified by the greater damping effect of viscosity on short waves.

CHAPTER VIII

BESSEL FUNCTIONS

8.1. Consider the operator $p^{-n}\exp(1/p)$, where n is a real number. By our rules we can write it as

$$p^{-n}\exp p^{-1} = p^{-n}\sum_{r=0}^{\infty}\frac{p^{-r}}{\Pi(r)} = \sum_{r=0}^{\infty}\frac{p^{-(n+r)}}{\Pi(r)}$$

$$= \sum_{r=0}^{\infty}\frac{t^{n+r}}{\Pi(r)\,\Pi(n+r)} \qquad \text{......................(1)}$$

$$= E_n(t), \qquad \text{......................................(2)}$$

say, when $t>0$. By differentiating the series in powers of t we have

$$\frac{d}{dt}E_n(t) = E_{n-1}(t). \qquad \text{........................(3)}$$

The function $E_n(t)$ satisfies the differential equation

$$\frac{d^2y}{dt^2} - \frac{n-1}{t}\frac{dy}{dt} - \frac{y}{t} = 0. \qquad \text{.....................(4)}$$

The other solution of this equation may be taken as

$$F_n(t) = \sum_{r=0}^{\infty}\frac{t^r}{\Pi(r)\,\Pi(r-n)} = \sum_{r=0}^{\infty}\frac{p^{-r}}{\Pi(r-n)}, \qquad \text{.........(5)}$$

unless n is an integer.

In the form of a complex integral,

$$E_n(t) = \frac{1}{2\pi\iota}\int_M \exp\left(\lambda t + \frac{1}{\lambda}\right)\frac{d\lambda}{\lambda^{n+1}}, \qquad \text{...............(6)}$$

where M passes round the origin on the positive side and proceeds to $-\infty$ at the ends. If t is positive this definition is equivalent to the series (1) without restriction on n.

Now if we replace t by $(\frac{1}{2}z)^2$,

$$E_n(\tfrac{1}{4}z^2) = (\tfrac{1}{2}z)^n\sum_{r=0}^{\infty}\frac{(\frac{1}{2}z)^{n+2r}}{\Pi(r)\,\Pi(n+r)}$$

$$= (\tfrac{1}{2}z)^n I_n(z), \qquad \text{..............................(7)}$$

where $I_n(z)$ is now the modified Bessel function, satisfying the differential equation

$$z\frac{d}{dz}\left(z\frac{dy}{dz}\right) - (z^2+n^2)\,y = 0. \qquad \text{..................(8)}$$

From (6)

$$I_n(z) = (\tfrac{1}{2}z)^{-n} \frac{1}{2\pi\iota} \int_M \exp\left(\frac{1}{4}\lambda z^2 + \frac{1}{\lambda}\right) \frac{d\lambda}{\lambda^{n+1}}, \quad \text{.........(9)}$$

which is equivalent to Schläfli's form*. Put also

$$\tfrac{1}{2}\lambda z = \kappa. \quad \text{..............................(10)}$$

Then

$$I_n(z) = \frac{1}{2\pi\iota} \int_M \exp \tfrac{1}{2} z \left(\kappa + \frac{1}{\kappa}\right) \frac{d\kappa}{\kappa^{n+1}}, \quad \text{............(11)}$$

if we take for z the positive value of $(2t)^{\frac{1}{2}}$. Now when λ is real and positive κ is real and positive; put now

$$\frac{1}{2}\left(\kappa + \frac{1}{\kappa}\right) = \mu. \quad \text{..........................(12)}$$

Then

$$\kappa = \mu + (\mu^2 - 1)^{\frac{1}{2}}, \quad \text{......................(13)}$$

the positive sign being taken for μ positive and greater than 1. Then when μ is $+\infty$, κ is $+\infty$, and as κ describes a large circle the arguments of κ and μ are nearly equal. Thus the path M for κ is equivalent to the path M for μ, provided only that we make it cross the real axis at a value of μ greater than $+1$.

Then

$$I_n(z) = \frac{1}{2\pi\iota} \int_M \exp(\mu z) \frac{d\mu}{(\mu^2 - 1)^{\frac{1}{2}} \{\mu + (\mu^2 - 1)^{\frac{1}{2}}\}^n}, \quad \text{......(14)}$$

whence, in operational form,

$$I_n(t) = \frac{p}{(p^2 - 1)^{\frac{1}{2}} \{p + (p^2 - 1)^{\frac{1}{2}}\}^n}. \quad \text{...............(15)}$$

This can be expanded in descending powers of p, and therefore corresponds to a series of ascending powers of t which will converge for all values of t, real or complex, and may be taken as the definition of the function. If n is fractional we remove ambiguity as to the argument by making $I_n(t)$ real and positive when t is real and positive. The coefficients are determined by (7); thus

$$I_n(t) = \sum_{r=0}^{\infty} \frac{(\frac{1}{2}t)^{n+2r}}{\Pi(r)\,\Pi(n+r)}. \quad \text{.................(16)}$$

The relation (3) is equivalent to

$$\frac{d}{dt}\{t^n I_n(t)\} = t^n I_{n-1}(t), \quad \text{....................(17)}$$

a familiar recurrence relation.

* Watson, *Bessel Functions*, 175–6 and 181.

If in (16) we replace n by $-n$, we obtain $I_{-n}(t)$, which is easily seen to be another solution of (8); but if n is a positive integer $\Pi(-n+r)$ is infinite for all values of r from 0 to $n-1$, so that the first n terms of the series for $I_{-n}(t)$ vanish, and the remainder are identical with $I_n(t)$.

8.2. Now consider

$$\phi(t) = \frac{1}{2\pi\iota}\int_N \exp(\mu t) \frac{d\mu}{(\mu^2-1)^{\frac{1}{2}}\{\mu+(\mu^2-1)^{\frac{1}{2}}\}^n}, \quad \text{......(1)}$$

taken along any path in the μ plane. We have

$$t\frac{d}{dt}\left(t\frac{d\phi}{dt}\right) - (t^2+n^2)\phi = \frac{1}{2\pi\iota}\int_N \exp(\mu t)\frac{t^2\mu^2+t\mu-t^2-n^2}{(\mu^2-1)^{\frac{1}{2}}\{\mu+(\mu^2-1)^{\frac{1}{2}}\}^n}d\mu. \quad \text{......(2)}$$

But

$$\frac{t^2(\mu^2-1)+t\mu-n^2}{(\mu^2-1)^{\frac{1}{2}}\{\mu+(\mu^2-1)^{\frac{1}{2}}\}^n}e^{\mu t} = \frac{d}{d\mu}\left\{\frac{(\mu^2-1)^{\frac{1}{2}}}{\{\mu+(\mu^2-1)^{\frac{1}{2}}\}^n}\frac{d}{d\mu}e^{\mu t}\right\} + \frac{d}{d\mu}\frac{ne^{\mu t}}{\{\mu+(\mu^2-1)^{\frac{1}{2}}\}^n}, \quad \text{......(3)}$$

so that the integral is the difference between the values at the limits of

$$\frac{(\mu^2-1)^{\frac{1}{2}}t+n}{\{\mu+(\mu^2-1)^{\frac{1}{2}}\}^n}e^{\mu t}. \quad \text{........................(4)}$$

If then the path N is such that this quantity has the same value at both ends, $\phi(t)$ will be a solution of the differential equation. Now the integrand in $\phi(t)$ has branch-points at ± 1, and also at infinity unless n is an integer. If then N is a closed contour and does not go round one or both of ± 1, $\phi(t)$ is identically zero. If t is positive and N begins and ends anywhere in the second and third quadrants respectively, and passes to the positive side of either branch-point, (4) vanishes at both limits on account of the factor $e^{\mu t}$, and $\phi(t)$ satisfies the differential equation.

8.21. Let N be the loop M already considered. Then $\phi(t)$ is $I_n(t)$. We may contract the loop vertically till it becomes the two sides of the

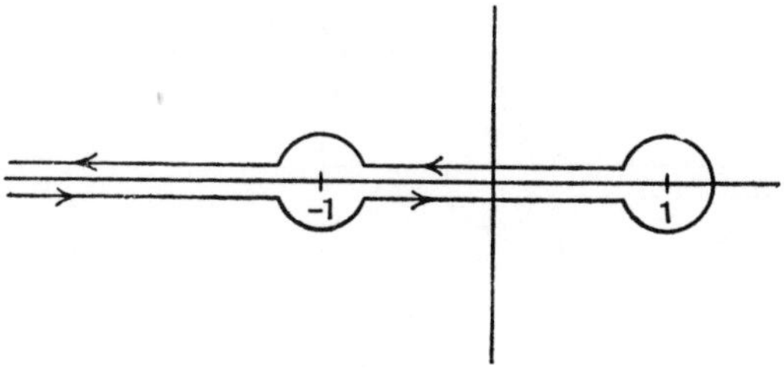

Fig. 8.

real axis from $-\infty$ to $+1$, with small circular arcs about ± 1, as in Fig. 8. On the lower side from $-\infty$ to -1, we can put $\mu = e^{-\iota\pi}\cosh v$; $(\mu^2-1)^{\frac{1}{2}} = e^{-\iota\pi}\sinh v$, and this part of the integral gives

$$\frac{1}{2\pi\iota}\int_\infty^0 e^{n\iota\pi}e^{-t\cosh v}e^{-nv}\,dv = -\frac{1}{2\pi\iota}\int_0^\infty e^{n\iota\pi}e^{-t\cosh v}e^{-nv}\,dv. \quad \text{...(5)}$$

From -1 to $-\infty$, on the upper side of the axis, we take similarly $\mu = e^{\iota\pi}\cosh v$, $(\mu^2-1)^{\frac{1}{2}} = e^{\iota\pi}\sinh v$, and the integral is

$$\frac{1}{2\pi\iota}\int_0^\infty e^{-n\iota\pi}e^{-t\cosh v}e^{-nv}\,dv.$$

The two parts together give $-\frac{1}{\pi}\sin n\pi\int_0^\infty e^{-t\cosh v}e^{-nv}\,dv$.

When we traverse the small semicircle below -1, μ and $\mu-1$ keep the same argument, bnt that of $\mu+1$ increases from $-\pi$ to 0. Hence from -1 to $+1$ we can put $\mu = e^{-\iota\pi}\cos\theta$, $(\mu^2-1)^{\frac{1}{2}} = e^{-\frac{1}{2}\iota\pi}\sin\theta$, with θ increasing from 0 to π. The corresponding part of the integral is

$$\frac{1}{2\pi}\int_0^\pi e^{n\iota\pi}e^{-t\cos\theta}e^{-n\iota\theta}\,d\theta = \frac{1}{2\pi}\int_0^\pi e^{t\cos\theta}e^{n\iota\theta}\,d\theta.$$

On approaching $+1$, μ is real and positive, while $(\mu^2-1)^{\frac{1}{2}}$ still has argument $-\frac{1}{2}\pi$. On traversing the circle about $+1$ we increase the argument of $(\mu^2-1)^{\frac{1}{2}}$ by π. Hence on the path from $+1$ to -1 we put $\mu = \cos\theta$, $(\mu^2-1)^{\frac{1}{2}} = e^{\frac{1}{2}\iota\pi}\sin\theta$ with θ increasing from 0 to π, and the corresponding part of the integral is $\frac{1}{2\pi}\int_0^\pi e^{t\cos\theta}e^{-n\iota\theta}\,d\theta$. The two last parts together give $\frac{1}{\pi}\int_0^\pi \cos n\theta\, e^{t\cos\theta}\,d\theta$, and in all

$$I_n(t) = \frac{1}{\pi}\int_0^\pi \cos n\theta\, e^{t\cos\theta}\,d\theta - \frac{1}{\pi}\sin n\pi\int_0^\infty e^{-nv}e^{-t\cosh v}\,dv. \quad \text{...(6)}$$

8.22. By 8.2 we may alternately take N to be a loop about -1 alone, as in Fig. 9.

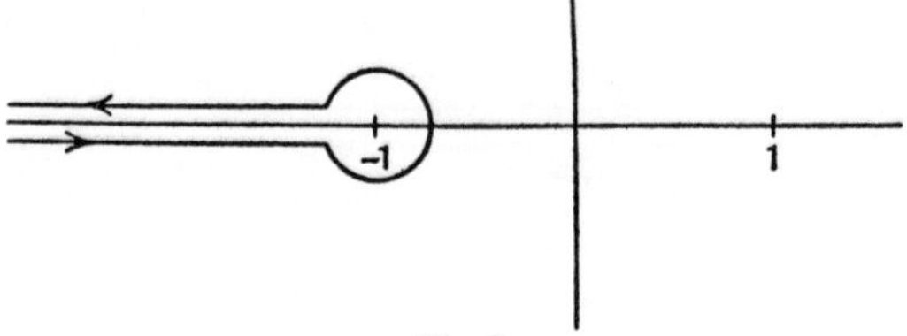

Fig. 9.

The contribution to the integral from the lower side of the path is as before. That from the upper side is different, for in describing the circle about -1, μ keeps the same argument, while that of $(\mu^2-1)^{\frac{1}{2}}$ increases by π, so that on the upper side we can put $\mu = e^{-\iota\pi}\cosh v$, $(\mu^2-1)^{\frac{1}{2}} = \sinh v$, and the integral is $-\frac{1}{2\pi\iota}\int_0^\infty e^{n\iota\pi} e^{-t\cosh v} e^{nv}\, dv$. Thus in this case

$$\phi(t) = -\frac{1}{2\pi\iota}\int_0^\infty e^{n\iota\pi} e^{-t\cosh v} e^{-nv}\, dv - \frac{1}{2\pi\iota}\int_0^\infty e^{n\iota\pi} e^{-t\cosh v} e^{nv}\, dv$$

$$= -\frac{1}{\pi\iota}\int_0^\infty e^{n\iota\pi}\cosh nv\, e^{-t\cosh v}\, dv. \quad\text{.........................(7)}$$

Now if in (6) we replace n by $-n$ we have

$$I_{-n}(t) = \frac{1}{\pi}\int_0^\pi \cos n\theta\, e^{t\cos\theta}\, d\theta + \frac{1}{\pi}\sin n\pi \int_0^\infty e^{nv} e^{-t\cosh v}\, dv, \quad\text{...(8)}$$

whence

$$I_{-n}(t) - I_n(t) = \frac{2}{\pi}\sin n\pi \int_0^\infty \cosh nv\, e^{-t\cosh v}\, dv$$

$$= \sin n\pi \,.\, K_n(t), \quad\text{.........................(9)}$$

say. Then in (7) we can write

$$\phi(t) = -\frac{1}{2\iota} e^{n\iota\pi} K_n(t), \quad\text{....................(10)}$$

and we may take

$$K_n(t) = \frac{2}{\pi}\int_0^\infty \cosh nv\, e^{-t\cosh v}\, dv \quad\text{.................(11)}$$

as our second solution of the differential equation even in the cases where $I_{-n}(t)$ coalesces with $I_n(t)$. Then (6) and (11) express our two solutions in real form*.

If $t \to 0$, $K_n(t)$ evidently $\to \infty$, and therefore has a singularity at the origin. $I_n(t)$ and $K_n(t)$ are both essentially positive.

8.3. *Asymptotic Approximations.* If t is large, we can replace $e^{-t\cosh v}$ in (11) by $e^{-t}e^{-2t\sinh^2\frac{1}{2}v}$, which is always less than $e^{-t}e^{-\frac{1}{2}v^2 t}$. Hence the important values of this factor are concentrated within a range of v of order $t^{-\frac{1}{2}}$. Within such a range $\cosh nv$ may be replaced by unity provided n^2/t is small. Then to a first approximation

$$K_n(t) = \frac{2}{\pi}\int_0^\infty e^{-t} e^{-\frac{1}{2}v^2 t}\, dv = \frac{2}{\pi} e^{-t} \,.\, \tfrac{1}{2}\sqrt{\pi}\sqrt{\frac{2}{t}}$$

$$= \sqrt{\frac{2}{\pi t}}\, e^{-t}. \quad\text{.................(1)}$$

* This notation for K_n corresponds to Heaviside's. Most writers on Bessel functions drop the factor $2/\pi$; Watson adopts this practice though he recognizes it as unfortunate.

If we put $$K_n(t) = \sqrt{\frac{2}{\pi t}}\, e^{-t}\left(1 + \frac{a_1}{t} + \frac{a_2}{t^2} + \dots\right), \qquad \text{.........(2)}$$
substitute in the differential equation, and equate coefficients of powers of t, we find the coefficients a_1, a_2 in succession. We get

$$K_n(t) = \sqrt{\frac{2}{\pi t}}\, e^{-t}\left\{1 + \frac{4n^2 - 1^2}{1!\,8t} + \frac{(4n^2-1^2)(4n^2-3^2)}{2!\,(8t)^2} + \dots\right). \qquad \text{...(3)}$$

The series is formally divergent for all values of t, but if t is large the terms decrease to a minimum, and it can be shown that the error in stopping at any term is less than the next term.

Again, if t is large the first integral in (6) can be replaced, subject to n^2/t being small, by

$$I_n(t) = \frac{1}{\pi}\int_0^\pi e^t e^{-\frac{1}{2}t\theta^2}\, d\theta = \frac{e^t}{\sqrt{(2\pi t)}}. \qquad \text{.........(4)}$$

By a similar process to that used for $K_n(t)$ we can obtain an asymptotic formula

$$I_n(t) = \frac{e^t}{\sqrt{(2\pi t)}}\left\{1 - \frac{4n^2-1^2}{1!\,8t} + \frac{(4n^2-1^2)(4n^2-3^2)}{2!\,(8t)^2} - \dots\right\}. \qquad \text{...(5)}$$

8.31. If n^2/t is not small, cosh nv in (11) may become great before $\exp(-t\cosh v)$ has become small enough to swamp it. Then we can replace $K_n(t)$ nearly by

$$K_n(t) = \frac{1}{\pi}\int_0 \exp(nv - t\cosh v)\, dv = \frac{1}{\pi}\int_0^\infty \exp f(v)\, dv, \qquad \text{...(1)}$$

say, and the integrand has a maximum where

$$f'(v) = n - t\sinh v = 0. \qquad \text{.........(2)}$$

There

$$\sinh v = n/t\,;\ f''(v) = -\,t\cosh v;\ f(v) = n\sinh^{-1}\frac{n}{t} - (t^2+n^2)^{\frac{1}{2}}. \qquad \text{...(3)}$$

Thus $$K_n(t) = \sqrt{\frac{2}{\pi}}\left(\sqrt{1 + \frac{n^2}{t^2}} + \frac{n}{t}\right)^n e^{-(t^2+n^2)^{\frac{1}{2}}}\,(t^2+n^2)^{-\frac{1}{4}}. \qquad \text{...(4)}$$

To obtain an approximation to $I_n(t)$ we use 8.1 (14). We have

$$I_n(t) = \frac{1}{2\pi\iota}\int_M \exp\{f(\mu)\}\frac{d\mu}{(\mu^2-1)^{\frac{1}{2}}}, \qquad \text{.........(5)}$$

where $$f(\mu) = \mu t - n\log\{\mu + (\mu^2-1)^{\frac{1}{2}}\}. \qquad \text{.........(6)}$$

There is a saddle-point where

$$f'(\mu) = t - \frac{n}{(\mu^2-1)^{\frac{1}{2}}} = 0; \qquad \text{.........(7)}$$

there $$\mu = \left(1 + \frac{n^2}{t^2}\right)^{\frac{1}{2}};\ f''(\mu) = \frac{n\mu}{(\mu^2 - 1)^{\frac{3}{2}}} = \frac{t^2}{n}\left(\frac{t^2}{n^2} + 1\right)^{\frac{1}{2}}, \quad \text{......(8)}$$

$$f(\mu) = (t^2 + n^2)^{\frac{1}{2}} - n \log\left\{\left(1 + \frac{n^2}{t^2}\right)^{\frac{1}{2}} + \frac{n}{t}\right\}. \quad \text{............(9)}$$

Since $f''(\mu)$ is positive the path of steepest descent is parallel to the imaginary axis; we find

$$I_n(t) = \frac{1}{\sqrt{2\pi}}(t^2 + n^2)^{-\frac{1}{4}} e^{(t^2+n^2)^{\frac{1}{2}}} \left\{\left(1 + \frac{n^2}{t^2}\right)^{\frac{1}{2}} + \frac{n}{t}\right\}^{-n}. \quad \text{...(10)}$$

If t is kept constant and n is increased, the dominant factor in $K_n(t)$ is $(2n/t)^n e^{-n}$, which tends to infinity; the dominant factor in $I_n(t)$ is $e^n (2n/t)^{-n}$, which tends to zero.

8.32. We note that, if y_1 and y_2 are any two solutions of the differential equation, and

$$\psi(t) = y_1' y_2 - y_2' y_1, \quad \text{.......................(1)}$$

$$\frac{d\psi}{dt} = y_1'' y_2 - y_2'' y_1 = -\frac{1}{t}(y_1' y_2 - y_2' y_1) = -\frac{1}{t}\psi(t), \quad \text{......(2)}$$

so that $\psi(t)$ is of the form A/t, where A is a constant. If we take $y_1 = I_n(t)$, $y_2 = K_n(t)$, and use 8.3 (3) and (5), we find A by considering large values of t; then

$$I_n'(t) K_n(t) - I_n(t) K_n'(t) = 2/\pi t. \quad \text{..............(3)}$$

8.4. The ordinary Bessel functions may be treated similarly, starting from the operator

$$p^{-n} \exp(-1/p) = (\tfrac{1}{2}t)^n J_n(2t^{\frac{1}{2}}), \quad \text{..................(1)}$$

or $$\frac{p}{(p^2 + 1)^{\frac{1}{2}}\{p + (p^2 + 1)^{\frac{1}{2}}\}^n} = J_n(t). \quad \text{..............(2)}$$

But when (2) is converted into a complex integral the branch-points are at $\pm \iota$, and the discussions of 8.21 and 8.22 need modification. This function satisfies the standard Bessel equation

$$t\frac{d}{dt}\left(t\frac{dy}{dt}\right) + (t^2 - n^2)y = 0,$$

and is fully treated in the standard works of Watson and of Gray, Mathews, and MacRobert.

8.5. In physical problems Bessel functions usually arise with arguments $p\varpi/c$. The foregoing work is still applicable because when an operational solution is interpreted as a complex integral p is replaced by a number with a positive real part. Then the factor $e^{\mu t}$ in the integrand is replaced by one that still tends exponentially to zero at $\mu = -\infty$, and the integral expressions survive without alteration. The importance of $K_n(p\varpi/c)$ is indicated by the factor $\exp\left(-\frac{p\varpi}{c}\right)$ in its asymptotic expansion, showing that it represents a diverging wave. In this expansion the factor $(p\varpi/c)^{r+\frac{1}{2}}$ in the denominator yields $t^{r+\frac{1}{2}}/\Pi(r+\frac{1}{2})$ in the interpretation, and the extra Π function in the denominator often saves the convergence.

8.51. A wave spreading out symmetrically from a point source gives a velocity potential depending on the operator

$$\phi = \frac{1}{r} e^{-pr/c}. \qquad (1)$$

Now suppose that a disturbance occurs at time 0 all along the axis of z, giving a disturbance of the form (1) per unit length. Then if ζ is the z-coordinate of the place where the disturbance starts, the disturbance at a point on the plane $z=0$ distant ϖ from the axis is

$$\phi = \int_{-\infty}^{\infty} \frac{1}{r} e^{-pr/c}\, d\zeta. \qquad (2)$$

Now put

$$r = \varpi \cosh v, \quad \zeta = \varpi \sinh v. \qquad (3)$$

Then

$$\phi = 2\int_0^{\infty} \exp\left(-\frac{p\varpi}{c}\cosh v\right) dv$$

$$= \pi K_0\left(\frac{p\varpi}{c}\right). \qquad (4)$$

If the intensity of the source is proportional to $\cos \lambda\zeta$, we write on the plane $z=0$,

$$\phi = \int_{-\infty}^{\infty} \frac{1}{r} \cos \lambda\zeta e^{-pr/c} d\zeta$$

$$= 2\int_0^{\infty} \cos(\lambda\varpi \sinh v) \exp\left(-\frac{p\varpi}{c}\cosh v\right) dv. \qquad (5)$$

Split the cosine into exponential terms and put

$$\frac{p\varpi}{c} = \gamma \cos \alpha; \quad \lambda\varpi = \gamma \sin \alpha. \qquad (6)$$

Then

$$\phi = \int_0^{\infty} \{e^{-\gamma \cosh(v-\iota\alpha)} + e^{-\gamma\cosh(v+\iota\alpha)}\}\, dv$$

$$= \int_{-\infty}^{\infty} e^{-\gamma\cosh(v-\iota\alpha)}\, dv, \qquad (7)$$

which is independent of α for $-\frac{1}{2}\pi < \alpha < \frac{1}{2}\pi$, and therefore

$$= 2\int_0^\infty e^{-\gamma \cosh v}\, dv$$

$$= \pi K_0 \left\{\left(\frac{p^2}{c^2} + \lambda^2\right)^{\frac{1}{2}} \varpi\right\}. \quad \text{......................(8)}$$

For a point with coordinate z we can put

$$\zeta = z + z' \quad \text{..............................(9)}$$

and $$\cos \lambda\zeta = \cos \lambda z \cos \lambda z' - \sin \lambda z \sin \lambda z'. \quad \text{............(10)}$$

The point is on the plane $z' = 0$, and we can repeat the process; evidently by symmetry the term in $\sin \lambda z'$ contributes nothing, and

$$\phi = \pi K_0 \left\{\left(\frac{p^2}{c^2} + \lambda^2\right)^{\frac{1}{2}} \varpi\right\} \cos \lambda z. \quad \text{...............(11)}$$

If the source has unit intensity between $\zeta = \pm h$ and zero elsewhere, we can write the intensity as

$$\frac{1}{2\pi\iota}\int_L \{e^{\lambda(\zeta+h)} - e^{\lambda(\zeta-h)}\}\frac{d\lambda}{\lambda} = \frac{1}{\pi\iota}\int_L e^{\lambda\zeta} \sinh \lambda h \frac{d\lambda}{\lambda}$$

$$= \frac{2}{\pi}\int_0^\infty \cos \lambda\zeta \sin \lambda h \frac{d\lambda}{\lambda}. \quad \text{...(12)}$$

Thus $$\phi = 2\int_0^\infty \cos \lambda z \sin \lambda h\, K_0\left\{\left(\frac{p^2}{c^2} + \lambda^2\right)^{\frac{1}{2}} \varpi\right\}\frac{d\lambda}{\lambda}. \quad \text{......(13)}$$

If h becomes very small we have for the disturbance due to unit intensity over the short range $\pm h$,

$$\phi = 2h\int_0^\infty \cos \lambda z\, K_0 \left\{\left(\frac{p^2}{c^2} + \lambda^2\right)^{\frac{1}{2}} \varpi\right\} d\lambda. \quad \text{.........(14)}$$

8.52. We can put 8.51 (1) in an alternative form in cylindrical coordinates. On the axis of z, with z positive, we have

$$\frac{1}{r}e^{-\kappa r/c} = \frac{1}{z}e^{-\kappa z/c} = \int_{\kappa/c}^\infty e^{-\lambda z}\, d\lambda. \quad \text{...............(1)}$$

Also the solution of the equation

$$\nabla^2\phi = \frac{\kappa^2\phi}{c^2} \quad \text{..............................(2)}$$

that is equal to $e^{-\lambda z}$ when $\varpi = 0$ is $e^{-\lambda z} J_0\left\{\left(\lambda^2 - \frac{\kappa^2}{c^2}\right)^{\frac{1}{2}} \varpi\right\}$. Hence

$$\frac{1}{r}e^{-\kappa r/c} = \int_{\kappa/c}^\infty e^{-\lambda z} J_0 \left\{\left(\lambda^2 - \frac{\kappa^2}{c^2}\right)^{\frac{1}{2}} \varpi\right\} d\lambda$$

$$= \int_0^\infty e^{-(k^2+\kappa^2/c^2)^{\frac{1}{2}} z} J_0(k\varpi) \frac{k\, dk}{(k^2 + \kappa^2/c^2)^{\frac{1}{2}}},$$

whence $\frac{1}{r} H\left(t - \frac{r}{c}\right)$ is expressible in cylindrical coordinates.

8.6. *The Submarine Cable.* The submarine cable is a uniform conductor with self-induction, capacity, resistance, and leakage. At distance x from the end suppose that the charge per unit length is y, the potential V, and the current i. Then the following equations hold:

$$y = kV, \qquad \text{(1)}$$

$$l\frac{di}{dt} + ri = -\frac{\partial V}{\partial x}, \qquad \text{(2)}$$

$$\frac{\partial y}{\partial t} = -\frac{\partial i}{\partial x} - sV. \qquad \text{(3)}$$

l, k, r are the self-induction, capacity, and resistance per unit length. The leakage is such that a potential V produces a current sV per unit length escaping through the insulation. Up to $t = 0$, y, i, and V are zero; afterwards V is raised to V_0, which may be a function of t, at $x = 0$. Then the subsidiary equations are

$$(lp + r)\, i = -\frac{\partial V}{\partial x}; \quad (kp + s)\, V = -\frac{\partial i}{\partial x}; \qquad \text{(4)}$$

whence

$$\frac{\partial^2 V}{\partial x^2} = (lp + r)(kp + s)\, V. \qquad \text{(5)}$$

Put

$$(lp + r)(kp + s) = q^2 = lk\{(p + \rho)^2 - \sigma^2\}. \qquad \text{(6)}$$

Then the operational solution is

$$V = e^{-qx} V_0. \qquad \text{(7)}$$

If the self-induction and leakage are negligible we can put $l = 0$, $s = 0$, and $q^2 = krp$. Then the solution has the same form as for conduction of heat. This condition occurs in ordinary telegraph wires. If in this case

$$V_0 = H(t),$$

$$V = 1 - \operatorname{erf} \frac{x}{2(krt)^{\frac{1}{2}}}. \qquad \text{(8)}$$

In the general case we put

$$lk = 1/c^2. \qquad \text{(9)}$$

Since $\rho + \sigma$ and $\rho - \sigma$ are equal to r/l and s/k, which are both positive, ρ is positive. We can without ambiguity take σ positive; then $\sigma < \rho$. If one of r/l and s/k is zero, $\sigma = \rho$; if both are equal, $\sigma = 0$. These are the extreme cases.

If $\sigma = 0$ we have simply

$$V = \exp\left\{-(p + \rho)\frac{x}{c}\right\}. V_0$$

$$= e^{-\rho x/c}\, V_0\left(t - \frac{x}{c}\right). \qquad \text{(10)}$$

Then the variation of V with time at distance x from the origin is an exact copy of that at the end except for the delay x/c and the constant attenuation factor $e^{-\rho x/c}$. This is the *distortionless cable.*

If σ is not zero we may take

$$V_0 = H(t),$$

and the solution is

$$V = \exp\left[-\frac{x}{c}\{(p+\rho)^2-\sigma^2\}^{\frac{1}{2}}\right] \quad\text{.......................(11)}$$

$$= \frac{1}{2\pi\iota}\int_L \exp\left[\lambda t - \frac{x}{c}\{(\lambda+\rho)^2-\sigma^2\}^{\frac{1}{2}}\right]\frac{d\lambda}{\lambda}. \quad\text{.........(12)}$$

The form (11) can be treated by expanding in powers of σ^2; the solution is

$$V = e^{-\rho x/c}\left[1 + \frac{\sigma^2 x}{2c}\left(t - \frac{x}{c}\right) + \dots\right], \quad\text{............(13)}$$

the terms, which are all positive, rising in powers of $\frac{\sigma^2 x}{c}\left(t-\frac{x}{c}\right)$ and $\sigma^2\left(t-\frac{x}{c}\right)^2$. So long as these numbers are small, this series may be useful. But if $\sigma x/c$ is large the series is not a useful form for any appreciable range of t after the arrival of the disturbance.

The form (12) may be treated by putting

$$\lambda = \mu - \rho. \quad\text{..............................(14)}$$

Then $$V = \frac{e^{-\rho t}}{2\pi\iota}\int_L \exp\left\{\mu t - \frac{x}{c}(\mu^2-\sigma^2)^{\frac{1}{2}}\right\}\frac{d\mu}{\mu-\rho}. \quad\text{............(15)}$$

The integrand has branch points at $\mu = \pm\sigma$ and a pole at $\mu = \rho$. If we write

$$f(\mu) = \mu t - \frac{x}{c}(\mu^2-\sigma^2)^{\frac{1}{2}}, \quad\text{..................(16)}$$

$$f'(\mu) = t - \frac{\mu x}{c(\mu^2-\sigma^2)^{\frac{1}{2}}}, \quad\text{....................(17)}$$

$$f''(\mu) = \frac{\sigma^2 x}{c(\mu^2-\sigma^2)^{\frac{3}{2}}}, \quad\text{.......................(18)}$$

then $f'(\mu)$ vanishes at $\mu = \mu_0$, where

$$\mu_0 = \sigma\left(1 - \frac{x^2}{c^2t^2}\right)^{-\frac{1}{2}}. \quad\text{.......................(19)}$$

Whenever $t > x/c$, μ_0 is greater than σ. If t is just greater than x/c, μ_0 is large; if t is large, μ_0 approaches σ, which is in general less than ρ. Hence for values of t greater than some critical value μ_0 is less than ρ, and a path through μ_0 parallel to the imaginary axis will have ρ on its right, and the pole there must be allowed for separately. This value is given by

$$ct/x=(1-\sigma^2/\rho^2)^{-\frac{1}{2}}. \qquad\qquad (20)$$

We have

$$f(\mu_0)=\sigma t\left(1-\frac{x^2}{c^2t^2}\right)^{\frac{1}{2}}, \qquad\qquad (21)$$

$$f''(\mu_0)=\frac{c^2t^3}{\sigma x^2}\left(1-\frac{x^2}{c^2t^2}\right)^{\frac{3}{2}}. \qquad\qquad (22)$$

On a path through μ_0 parallel to the imaginary axis, considerable values of the exponential are spread over a range of order $\{f''(\mu_0)\}^{-\frac{1}{2}}$ or $\left(\frac{\sigma x^2}{c^2t^3}\right)^{\frac{1}{2}}\left(1-\frac{x^2}{c^2t^2}\right)^{-\frac{3}{4}}$. This bears to μ_0 the ratio $\frac{x}{ct\,(\sigma t)^{\frac{1}{2}}}\left(1-\frac{x^2}{c^2t^2}\right)^{-\frac{1}{4}}$, which is large if t is just greater than x/c but becomes small if t is large. In the former case we cannot neglect the variation of $\mu-\rho$ on the path of steepest descent. In the latter, the ratio is much less than $(\sigma x/c)^{-\frac{1}{2}}$ which we have already assumed small. Then the contribution from the neighbourhood of μ_0 is

$$-\frac{e^{-\rho t}}{2\pi(\rho-\mu_0)}\exp f(\mu_0)\,.\left\{\frac{2\pi}{f''(\mu_0)}\right\}^{\frac{1}{2}}$$

$$=-\left(\frac{\sigma x^2}{2\pi c^2t^3}\right)^{\frac{1}{2}}\left(1-\frac{x^2}{c^2t^2}\right)^{-\frac{3}{4}}\left\{\rho-\sigma\left(1-\frac{x^2}{c^2t^2}\right)^{-\frac{1}{2}}\right\}^{-1}$$

$$\times\exp\left\{\sigma t\left(1-\frac{x^2}{c^2t^2}\right)^{\frac{1}{2}}-\rho t\right\}. \qquad\qquad (23)$$

But the pole at ρ is to the right of the path and makes a further contribution

$$e^{-\rho t}\exp\left\{\rho t-\frac{x}{c}(\rho^2-\sigma^2)^{\frac{1}{2}}\right\}=\exp\left\{-\frac{x}{c}(\rho^2-\sigma^2)^{\frac{1}{2}}\right\}. \quad\ldots(24)$$

This is independent of the time. The expression (23) tends to zero when t is large, since $\rho>\sigma$. The sum of (24) and (23) is an asymptotic form of the solution when t is greater than the value given by (20); and the potential approximates to the steady value (24) if $(ct/x)^2$ exceeds $(1-\sigma^2/\rho^2)^{-1}$. Thus the time needed for the disappearance of the variable part is of order $\frac{x}{c}\left(1-\frac{\sigma^2}{\rho^2}\right)^{-\frac{1}{2}}$.

In the critical case where either the resistance or the leakage is zero, $\sigma=\rho$, and this time is infinite, so that the value (24) is never approached.

We can obtain a solution in a series from (15) by writing

$$\mu^2-\sigma^2=(2\nu-\mu)^2. \qquad\qquad (25)$$

Then $$\mu = \nu + \frac{\sigma^2}{4\nu}; \ 2\nu - \mu = \nu - \frac{\sigma^2}{4\nu}, \quad \text{......(26)}$$

$$V = \frac{e^{-\rho t}}{2\pi\iota}\int_L \exp\left\{\nu\left(t - \frac{x}{c}\right) + \frac{\sigma^2}{4\nu}\left(t + \frac{x}{c}\right)\right\} \frac{4\nu^2 - \sigma^2}{4\nu^2 - 4\nu\rho + \sigma^2}\frac{d\nu}{\nu} \quad \text{......(27)}$$

$$= \frac{e^{-\rho t}}{2\pi\iota}\int_L \exp\left(\nu t_1 + \frac{\sigma^2}{4\nu}t_2\right)\left(1 + \frac{\nu_1}{\nu - \nu_1} + \frac{\nu_2}{\nu - \nu_2}\right)\frac{d\nu}{\nu}, \quad \text{......(28)}$$

where $$t_1 = t - \frac{x}{c}; \ t_2 = t + \frac{x}{c}; \quad \text{......(29)}$$

$$2\nu_1 = \rho + (\rho^2 - \sigma^2)^{\frac{1}{2}}; \quad 2\nu_2 = \rho - (\rho^2 - \sigma^2)^{\frac{1}{2}}. \quad \text{......(30)}$$

But we have the general expansion

$$\exp\left\{\tfrac{1}{2}z\left(\lambda + \frac{1}{\lambda}\right)\right\} = \sum_{n=-\infty}^{\infty} \lambda^n I_n(z), \quad \text{......(31)}$$

whence

$$\exp\left(\nu t_1 + \frac{\sigma^2}{4\nu}t_2\right) = \sum_{n=-\infty}^{\infty}\left\{\frac{2\nu}{\sigma}\left(\frac{ct - x}{ct + x}\right)^{\frac{1}{2}}\right\}^n I_n\left\{\sigma\left(t^2 - \frac{x^2}{c^2}\right)^{\frac{1}{2}}\right\}. \quad (32)$$

The integral in (28), when t_1 is positive, may be taken around any circle large enough to include the singularities at $\nu = 0$, ν_1, ν_2. But negative values of n make no contribution to the contour integral; whence

$$V = \frac{e^{-\rho t}}{2\pi\iota}\int_C \sum_{n=0}^{\infty}\left\{\frac{2\nu}{\sigma}\left(\frac{t_1}{t_2}\right)^{\frac{1}{2}}\right\}^n I_n\{\sigma(t_1 t_2)^{\frac{1}{2}}\}\left(1 + \frac{\nu_1}{\nu - \nu_1} + \frac{\nu_2}{\nu - \nu_2}\right)\frac{d\nu}{\nu}. \quad \text{......(33)}$$

But $$\left.\begin{aligned}\frac{1}{2\pi\iota}\int_C \nu^n \frac{d\nu}{\nu} &= 0 \text{ if } n > 0\\ \text{and } &= 1 \text{ if } n = 0\end{aligned}\right\}; \quad \text{......(34)}$$

$$\left.\begin{aligned}\frac{1}{2\pi\iota}\int_C \nu^n \frac{\nu_1}{\nu - \nu_1}\frac{d\nu}{\nu} = \frac{1}{2\pi\iota}\int \nu^n \sum_{r=1}^{\infty}\left(\frac{\nu_1}{\nu}\right)^r \frac{d\nu}{\nu} &= \nu_1^n \text{ if } n > 0\\ \text{and } &= 0 \text{ if } n = 0\end{aligned}\right\}. \quad (35)$$

Hence

$$V = e^{-\rho t}\left[I_0\{\sigma(t_1 t_2)^{\frac{1}{2}}\} + \sum_{n=1}^{\infty}\left\{\frac{2}{\sigma}\left(\frac{t_1}{t_2}\right)^{\frac{1}{2}}\right\}^n (\nu_1^n + \nu_2^n) I_n\{\sigma(t_1 t_2)^{\frac{1}{2}}\}\right]. \quad (36)$$

In the case where $\sigma = 0$, each of the $(2/\sigma)^n I_n\{\sigma(t_1 t_2)^{\frac{1}{2}}\}$ reduces to its first term $\{(t_1 t_2)^{\frac{1}{2}}\}^n/n!$, $\nu_1 = \rho$, $\nu_2 = 0$, and

$$V = V_0 e^{-\rho t}\left(1 + \sum_{n=1}^{\infty}\left(\frac{t_1}{t_2}\right)^{\frac{1}{2}n}(\rho^n)\frac{(t_1 t_2)^{\frac{1}{2}n}}{n!}\right)$$

$$= V_0 e^{-\rho t}\left(1 + \sum_{n=1}^{\infty}\frac{(\rho t_1)^n}{n!}\right)$$

$$= V_0 e^{-\rho t} e^{\rho t_1} = V_0 e^{-\rho x/c}, \quad \text{......(37)}$$

agreeing with (10).

Alternatively if we replace $\partial/\partial t_1$ operationally by p_1, (28) is equivalent to

$$e^{-\rho t}\exp\frac{\sigma^2 t_2}{4p_1}\cdot\left(1+\sum_{r=1}^{\infty}\frac{\nu_1^r+\nu_2^r}{p_1^r}\right)H(t_1)$$

$$=e^{-\rho t}\sum_{n=0}^{\infty}\frac{1}{n!}\left(\frac{\sigma^2 t_2}{4p_1}\right)^n\left\{1+\sum_{r=1}^{\infty}\frac{\nu_1^r+\nu_2^r}{p_1^r}\right\}H(t_1)$$

$$=e^{-\rho t}\left\{\sum_{n=0}^{\infty}\frac{1}{n!}\left(\frac{\sigma^2 t_2}{4p_1}\right)^n+\sum_{n=0}^{\infty}\sum_{r=1}^{\infty}\frac{(\sigma^2 t_2)^n}{n!\,4^n}\frac{\nu_1^r+\nu_2^r}{p_1^{n+r}}\right\}H(t_1)$$

$$=e^{-\rho t}\left\{\sum_{n=0}^{\infty}\frac{(\frac{1}{4}\sigma^2 t_1 t_2)^n}{n!\;n!}+\sum_{n=0}^{\infty}\sum_{r=1}^{\infty}\frac{(\frac{1}{4}\sigma^2 t_1 t_2)^n}{n!\;(n+r)!}t_1^r(\nu_1^r+\nu_2^r)\right\},\qquad\ldots\ldots(38)$$

which on rearrangement gives the form (36).

8.7. The operational method raises numerous points concerning the solution of the differential equations of mathematical physics. Chapter I of this work suffices to show that it gives the correct results when the system has a finite number of degrees of freedom; but as soon as we proceed to continuous systems we find that the solution involves operators not expressible by series of negative powers of p, and the method of Chapter I is no longer available as a justification.

We have seen that in certain continuous systems the use of the partial differential equation is itself open to suspicion. Thus in a string the value of $\partial y/\partial x$ may be discontinuous at certain points, and $\partial^2 y/\partial x^2$ does not exist there and the differential equation is simply meaningless. The real problem that concerns us is not whether the operational method gives the correct solution of the partial differential equations, for these equations are themselves defective. The question is whether, if we use these equations, modified to allow for the initial conditions, and solve them by the operational method, the answer is correct for the actual physical system. We have to test the answer in relation to the physical problem, not in relation to the differential equations, which are themselves an imperfect statement of the problem and in any case only an intermediate stage in its solution. My own view is that most continuous systems should be regarded as the limits of discrete systems. Thus if we have a string loaded at intervals l with particles of mass ρl, and the displacement of the rth particle from the end is y_r, the equation of motion of a particle is

$$\ddot{y}_r=-\frac{c^2}{l^2}(2y_r-y_{r-1}-y_{r+1}),\qquad\ldots\ldots\ldots\ldots\ldots\ldots(1)$$

where $c^2=P/\rho$, P being the tension.

If we make l approach zero while ρ and c remain constant, the system approaches in the limit the continuous string with line-density ρ. If further the quantity on the right tends to a definite limit we can put $rl=x$, so that x is the distance of the particle from the end, and the equation takes the ordinary form

$$\frac{\partial^2 y}{\partial t^2}=c^2\frac{\partial^2 y}{\partial x^2}. \quad \text{.............................(2)}$$

But whether the limit $\partial^2 y/\partial x^2$ exists or not, (1) represents the equations of motion of a system with a finite number of degrees of freedom, and for any initial conditions there is an operational solution involving only powers of p^{-1}, and therefore certainly equivalent to the corresponding integral along the line L. It actually involves operators of the form *

$$\phi(p)=\left\{\left(1+\frac{p^2l^2}{4c^2}\right)^{\frac{1}{2}}+\frac{pl}{2c}\right\}^{-2r},$$

which can clearly be expanded in negative powers of p. But the corresponding function of λ, when l becomes very small, is for large values of r

$$\phi(\lambda)=\exp\left[-2r\log\left\{1+\frac{\lambda l}{2c}+O\left(\frac{\lambda^2l^2}{c^2}\right)\right\}\right]$$

$$=\exp\left[-2r\left\{\frac{\lambda l}{2c}+O\left(\frac{\lambda^2l^2}{c^2}\right)\right\}\right],$$

and therefore tends to $e^{-r\lambda l/c}$ or $e^{-\lambda x/c}$. Thus the limit of the solution is precisely Bromwich's interpretation, with $\phi(p)$ replaced by its formal limit $e^{-px/c}$. The operational solution is therefore justified as the limit of the actual solution for a discrete system.

* Jeffreys, *Proc. Camb. Phil. Soc.* 23, 1927, 768–778.

NOTE

ON THE NOTATION FOR THE ERROR FUNCTION OR PROBABILITY INTEGRAL

The notation Erf x is one that I adopted in 1916 under the impression that it was in general use, and I have since used it in several publications*. My definition was queried by a correspondent in 1925, and I have not succeeded in tracing its origin. I have, on the other hand, discovered a surprising confusion of other notations. The earliest, due to Gauss†, is

$$\Theta(z) = \frac{2}{\sqrt{\pi}} \int_0^z e^{-z^2}\, dz. \quad \text{.............................(1)}$$

No name is given to the function by Gauss, and there is no sign that he meant the notation to be permanent. Of modern writers, Carslaw, Brunt, and Coolidge use this notation. Fourier‡ gives

$$\psi R = \frac{1}{\sqrt{\pi}} \int_R^\infty e^{-r^2}\, dr, \quad \text{.............................(2)}$$

but has, so far as I have traced, no modern followers. Jahnke and Emde, in their tables, use

$$\Phi(x) = \frac{2}{\sqrt{\pi}} \int_0^x e^{-x^2}\, dx, \quad \text{.............................(3)}$$

and call this the Fehlerintegral. The same notation is widely used by other German writers. Whittaker and Robinson§ also use it and call the function the Error Function. The notation

$$\text{Erf}\, x = \int_x^\infty e^{-x^2}\, dx \quad \text{.............................(4)}$$

was introduced by J. W. L. Glaisher||, who also used¶

$$\text{Erfc}\, x = \int_0^x e^{-x^2}\, dx = \tfrac{1}{2}\sqrt{\pi} - \text{Erf}\, x. \quad \text{.....................(5)}$$

The latter function is also called erf x by R. Pendlebury**.

* *Phil. Mag.* 32, 1916, 579–585; 35, 1918, 273; 38, 1919, 718. *M.N.R.A.S.* 77, 1916, 95–97. *Proc. Roy. Soc.* A, 100, 1921, 125–6. *The Earth*, 1924, 1929.

† *Werke*, 4, 9. First published 1821.

‡ *Théorie Analytique de la Chaleur*, 1822, 458.

§ *Calculus of Observations*, 1924, 179.

|| *Phil. Mag.* (4), 42, 1871, 294–302.

¶ *Loc. cit.* 421–436.

** *Loc. cit.* 437–440.

Whittaker and Watson* use Glaisher's notation with the meanings of Erf and Erfc interchanged, while Jeans's† erf x is $\frac{2}{\sqrt{\pi}}$ times Glaisher's Erf. Numerous other writers use the integrals, but omit to give any special symbol or use only the non-committal "I." Heaviside‡ used erf x to denote the function (1) or (3).

It can hardly be denied, in view of the wide application of the error function to thermal conduction, the theory of errors, statistics, and the dynamical theory of gases, that it merits a distinctive notation. It is equally clear that none of those yet used has obtained general acceptance. Of them, it seems that those involving only the single letters Θ, Φ, Ψ are wholly undesirable. In dynamical problems these letters are in continual use for couples, while Φ is often wanted for a velocity potential and Ψ or ψ for a stream function; ψ is of course also often needed for an angle. Further, Θ has an established meaning already in the theory of elliptic functions, namely, the Theta Function of Jacobi, while Φ has another meaning in the theory of numbers. To avoid confusion in some of the applications of the function it seems necessary to use a combination of letters, and the only one in frequent use is Erf. On the other hand, as Dr Goldstein has pointed out to me, the capital letter is somewhat inconvenient in typing, and is not intrinsically useful, so erf has some advantage.

As to what function should be denoted by this symbol, the most convenient is indicated by the practice of the compilers of tables, such as Jahnke and Emde and Dale, who tabulate $\frac{2}{\sqrt{\pi}}\int_0^x e^{-u^2}\,du$. This is an odd function and becomes unity when $x=\infty$, two properties that make for analytical convenience and are connected with the fact that this form, including the factor $2\pi^{-\frac{1}{2}}$, usually occurs as such in the solutions of the relevant problems. Accordingly I think that, of the various notations proposed,

$$\operatorname{erf} x = \frac{2}{\sqrt{\pi}}\int_0^x e^{-u^2}\,du$$

is the most convenient, and is worthy of general adoption. It has also the recommendation that it has previously been used by Heaviside.

* *Modern Analysis*, 1915, 335.

† *Dynamical Theory of Gases*, 1921, 34.

‡ *Electromagnetic Theory*, 2, 51.

INTERPRETATIONS OF THE PRINCIPAL OPERATORS

$$p^{-n} H(t) = 0 \qquad t < 0$$
$$= \frac{t^n}{n!} \qquad t > 0.$$

$$\frac{p}{p-a} = e^{at}; \quad \frac{p}{(p-a)^n} = \frac{t^{n-1}}{(n-1)!} e^{at}; \quad \frac{a}{p-a} = e^{at} - 1.$$

$$\frac{p(p-\beta)}{(p-\beta)^2 + \gamma^2} = e^{\beta t} \cos \gamma t;$$

$$\frac{\gamma p}{(p-\beta)^2 + \gamma^2} = e^{\beta t} \sin \gamma t.$$

$$\frac{f(p)}{F(p)} = \frac{f(0)}{F(0)} + \sum_a \frac{f(a)}{aF'(a)} e^{at}.$$

$$\frac{1}{p-a} S(t) = e^{at} \int_0^t S(t) e^{-at} \, dt.$$

$$\frac{np}{p^2+n^2} = \sin nt; \quad \frac{p^2}{p^2+n^2} = \cos nt; \quad \frac{np}{p^2-n^2} = \sinh nt; \quad \frac{p^2}{p^2-n^2} = \cosh nt.$$

$$e^{-px} f(t) = f(t-x).$$

$$p^{\frac{1}{2}} = \frac{1}{\sqrt{\pi t}}; \quad p^{\frac{3}{2}} = -\frac{1}{2\sqrt{\pi}} t^{-\frac{3}{2}}; \quad p^{-\frac{1}{2}} = 2\sqrt{\frac{t}{\pi}}.$$

If $p = h^2 q^2$,

$$e^{-qx} = 1 - \operatorname{erf} \frac{x}{2ht^{\frac{1}{2}}}; \quad qe^{-qx} = \frac{1}{h(\pi t)^{\frac{1}{2}}} e^{-x^2/4h^2t};$$

$$\frac{1}{q} e^{-qx} = 2h \left(\frac{t}{\pi}\right)^{\frac{1}{2}} e^{-x^2/4h^2t} - x\left(1 - \operatorname{erf} \frac{x}{2ht^{\frac{1}{2}}}\right);$$

$$\frac{ae^{-qx}}{q+a} = 1 - \operatorname{erf} \frac{x}{2ht^{\frac{1}{2}}} - \exp(a^2h^2t + ax)\left\{1 - \operatorname{erf}\left(\frac{x}{2ht^{\frac{1}{2}}} + aht^{\frac{1}{2}}\right)\right\}.$$

$$\frac{p}{\{p+(p^2-1)^{\frac{1}{2}}\}^n (p^2-1)^{\frac{1}{2}}} = I_n(t); \quad \frac{p}{\{p+(p^2+1)^{\frac{1}{2}}\}^n (p^2+1)^{\frac{1}{2}}} = J_n(t).$$

TABLE of e^{-x^2}, erf x, $1 - \text{erf}\, x$, $\Phi_1(x)$, $\Phi_2(x)$,

where $\Phi_1(x) = \int_x^\infty (1 - \text{erf}\, x)\, dx, \quad \Phi_2(x) = \int_x^\infty \Phi_1(x)\, dx.$

x	e^{-x^2}	erf x	$1 - \text{erf}\, x$	$\Phi_1(x)$	$\Phi_2(x)$
0·0	1·0000	0·0000	1·0000	0·5641	0·2500
0·1	0·9990	0·1125	0·8875	0·4698	0·1984
0·2	0·9608	0·2227	0·7773	0·3866	0·1556
0·3	0·9139	0·3286	0·6714	0·3142	0·1206
0·4	0·8521	0·4284	0·5716	0·2521	0·09241
0·5	0·7788	0·5205	0·4795	0·1996	0·06990
0·6	0·6977	0·6039	0·3961	0·1559	0·05220
0·7	0·6126	0·6778	0·3222	0·1201	0·03846
0·8	0·5273	0·7421	0·2579	0·0911	0·02795
0·9	0·4449	0·7969	0·2031	0·0682	0·02003
1·0	0·3679	0·8427	0·1573	0·0502	0·01415
1·1	0·2982	0·8802	0·1198	0·0364	0·00985
1·2	0·2369	0·9103	0·0897	0·0260	0·00675
1·3	0·1845	0·9340	0·0660	0·0183	0·00455
1·4	0·1409	0·9523	0·0477	0·0126	0·00302
1·5	0·1054	0·9661	0·0339	0·0086	0·00197
1·6	0·0773	0·9763	0·0237	0·0057	0·00126
1·7	0·0556	0·9838	0·0162	0·0038	0·00079
1·8	0·0392	0·9891	0·0109	0·0024	0·00049
1·9	0·0270	0·9928	0·0072	0·0015	0·00029
2·0	0·0183	0·9953	0·0047	0·0009	0·00017
2·1	0·0121	0·9970	0·0030	0·0006	0·00010
2·2	0·0079	0·9981	0·0019	0·0003	0·00005
2·3	0·0050	0·9989	0·0011	0·0002	0·00003
2·4	0·0031	0·9993	0·0007	0·0001	0·00001
2·5	0·0020	0·9996	0·0004	0·0000	0·00001
2·6	0·0012	0·9998	0·0002		0·00000
2·7	0·0007	0·9999	0·0001		
2·8	0·0004	0·9999	0·0001		
2·9	0·0002	1·0000	0·0000		
3·0	0·0001	1·0000	0·0000		

BIBLIOGRAPHY

The following list refers only to papers where operational methods are used; references to other papers where problems similar to those of the present work are treated by non-operational methods will be found in the text. It can make no claim to completeness.

Oliver Heaviside, *On Operators in Physical Mathematics*, Proc. Roy. Soc. A, 52, 1893, 504–529; 54, 1894, 105–143. Fundamental notions and general theory: applications to the exponential function, Taylor's theorem, and Bessel functions. The arguments used are in many cases suggestive rather than demonstrative, and much in the papers would repay reinvestigation.

Electromagnetic Theory, 1, 466 pp., 1893; 2, 542 pp., 1899; 3, 519 pp., 1912. Published by "The Electrician," reprinted by Benn, 1922. The original edition is the better printed. The applications are mainly to electromagnetic waves, but heat conduction is also discussed, and much in the work can be extended to waves in general.

Electrical Papers, 1, 560 pp., 1892; 2, 587 pp., 1892.

T. J. I'A. Bromwich, *Normal Coordinates in Dynamical Systems*, Proc. Lond. Math. Soc. (2) 15, 1916, 401–448. Gives the first general justification of the operational method for systems with a finite number of degrees of freedom, and develops a formally equivalent method applicable to continuous systems. A rediscussion of the oscillations of dynamical systems is carried out, and presents several advantages over the ordinary method of normal coordinates. Several problems in wave propagation are solved.

Examples of Operational Methods in Mathematical Physics, Phil. Mag. (6) 37, 1919, 407–419. Finds the temperatures recorded by thermometers with spherical and cylindrical bulbs when the temperature outside is varying, and solves the problem of the induction balance.

The Problem of Random Flights, Phil. Mag. (6) 42, 1921, 432–435.

Symbolical Methods in the Theory of Conduction of Heat, Proc. Camb. Phil. Soc. 20, 1921, 411–427. The principal operators that arise in problems of heat conduction are interpreted, and the problem of a sphere cooling by radiation from the surface is solved.

A certain Series of Bessel Functions, Proc. Lond. Math. Soc. (2) 25, 1926, 103–114. Discusses the vibration of a circular membrane with given initial conditions.

Some Solutions of the Electromagnetic Equations, and of the Elastic Equations, with Applications to the Problem of Secondary Waves, Proc. Lond. Math. Soc. 28, 1928, 438–475.

A new Method for solving Two-Dimensional Problems of Physical Types, Proc. Lond. Math. Soc. 30, 1929, 165–173.

Motion of a Sphere in a Viscous Fluid, Proc. Camb. Phil. Soc. 25, 1929, 369–383.

The Application of Operational Methods to some Electrical Problems in Diffusion, Proc. Lond. Math. Soc. 31, 1930, 209–216.

An Application of Heaviside's Methods to Viscous Fluid Motion, Journ. Lond. Math. Soc. 5, 1930, 10–13.

E. P. Adams, *Some Applications of Heaviside's Operational Methods*, Proc. Amer. Phil. Soc. 62, 1923, 26–47. Problems of conduction in spheres and cylinders with radiation absorbed and emitted from the surface.

Bevan B. Baker, *An Extension of Heaviside's Operational Method of Solving Differential Equations*, Proc. Edin. Math. Soc. 42, 1924, 95–103. The partial-fraction rule is extended to cases where the operand is not $H(t)$. See also note on the above paper by T. Kaucký, *loc. cit.* 43, 1925, 115–116, which considers operators in greater generality.

E. J. Berg, *Heaviside's Operators in Engineering and Physics*, J. Frank. Inst. 198, 1924, 647–702.

V. Bush, *Note on Operational Calculus*, J. Math. and Phys. 3, 1924, 95–107. Notices the non-commutative character of p and p^{-1}, and discusses its effects on some interpretations.

J. Carson, *Heaviside Operational Calculus*, Bell Sys. Tech. J. 1, 1922, 43–55.

A General Expansion Theorem for the Transient Oscillations of a Connected System, Phys. Rev. 10, 1917, 217–225.

Electric Circuit Theory and the Operational Calculus, Bell Sys. Tech. J. 4, 1925, 685–761; 5, 1926, 50–95, 336–384. A general discussion *ab initio*. The operational solution

$$\frac{1}{Z(p)}=A(x)$$

is interpreted as the solution of the integral equation

$$\frac{1}{\kappa Z(\kappa)}=\int_0^\infty A(x)\,e^{-\kappa x}\,dx.$$

This equation is then solved by known rules. Numerous electrical applications are given.

Electric Circuit Theory and the Operational Calculus, McGraw-Hill Book Co., New York, 1926.

Louis Cohen, *Electrical Oscillations in Lines*, J. Frank. Inst. 195, 1923, 45–58. *Alternating Current Cable Telegraphy*, *loc. cit.* 165–182. *Applications of Heaviside's Expansion Theorem*, *loc. cit.* 319–326. Contents sufficiently indicated by titles.

A. F. Crossley, *Operational Solution of some Problems in Viscous Fluid Motion*, Proc. Camb. Phil. Soc. 24, 1928, 231–235.

On the Motion of a Rotating Circular Cylinder filled with Viscous Fluid, Proc. Camb. Phil. Soc. 24, 1928, 480–488. The cylinder is closed at one end, but it is doubtful how long the motion determined can persist on account of the rise into importance of the second-order terms.

D. P. Dalzell, *Heaviside's Operational Method*, Proc. Phys. Soc. 42, 1930, 75–81. An elegant theoretical discussion, with some applications to integral equations.

Harold Jeffreys, *On Compressional Waves in Two Superposed Layers*, Proc. Camb. Phil. Soc. 23, 1926, 472–481. Discusses diffraction of an explosion wave at a plane boundary, with a seismological application.

Wave Propagation in Strings with Continuous and Concentrated Loads, Proc. Camb. Phil. Soc. 23, 1927, 768–778. Some of the results for continuous strings are obtained as the limits of those for light strings loaded regularly with heavy particles. It is found that the operator $e^{-\sigma x/c}$ arises as

$$\lim_{l\to 0}\left\{\left(1+\frac{\sigma^2 l^2}{4c^2}\right)^{\frac{1}{2}}+\frac{\sigma l}{2c}\right\}^{-2x/l},$$

when l tends to zero through such values as make x/l integral. This gives the rule 1.8 (5) in terms of definite integration.

The Earth's Thermal History, Gerlands Beiträge z. Geophysik, 18, 1927, 1–29. The problem of the cooling of the earth is rediscussed, with allowance for variation of conductivity with depth.

Paul Lévy, *Le Calcul Symbolique d'Heaviside*, Gauthier-Villars, Paris, 1926; also Bull. des Sciences Mathématiques, (2) 50, 1926, 174.

H. W. March, *The Heaviside Operational Calculus*, Bull. Am. Math. Soc. 33, 1927, 311–318. Proves that Bromwich's integral is the solution of Carson's integral equation, and derives several rules for interpretation from it. The author refers to a paper by K. W. Wagner, Archiv für Elektrotechnik, 4, 1916, 159–193, who seems to have obtained some of Bromwich's results independently. I have not seen the latter paper.

A. T. McKay, *Diffusion into an Infinite Plane Sheet subject to a surface condition*, Proc. Phys. Soc. 42, 1930, 547–555.

Balth. van der Pol, *A Simple Proof and an Extension of Heaviside's Operational Calculus for Invariable Systems*, Phil. Mag. 7, 1929, 1153–1162.

On the Operational Solution of Linear Differential Equations and an Investigation of the Properties of these solutions, Phil. Mag. 8, 1929, 861–898.

J. J. Smith, *The solution of Differential Equations by a method similar to Heaviside's*, J. Frank. Inst. 195, 1923, 815–850. General theory, with applications to electricity and heat conduction.

An analogy between Pure Mathematics and the Operational methods of Heaviside by means of the theory of H-Functions, J. Frank. Inst. 200, 1925, 519–536, 635–672, 775–814. Mainly theoretical, bearing, I think, more on the relation of the theory of functions of a real variable to mathematical physics in general than to Heaviside's methods in particular. The ideas are interesting and useful, though I am not in complete agreement with them. The last paper contains several physical applications.

Norbert Wiener, *The Operational Calculus*, Math. Ann. 95, 1925, 557–584. A critical discussion, beginning with a generalized Fourier integral. In some cases the interpretations of the operators differ from those of other workers.

The form of Fourier's theorem 2·31 (4) seems to have been given first by S. Pincherle, Memorie di Bologna, (4) 7, 1886, 393–442. G. H. Hardy deduces it from Mellin's inversion formula, Messenger of Mathematics, 50, 1921, 165–171.

INDEX TO AUTHORS

SUBJECT INDEX